HOW TO
BUILD HEALTHCARE
SYSTEMS

Titles in this series

HOW TO BUILD HEALTHCARE SYSTEMS

J. A. MUIR GRAY
Kt, CBE, DSc, MD
Consultant in Public Health
Director, Better Value Healthcare

Series Editor
ERICA ISON

OFFOX PRESS

First published 2011

Published by Offox Press for Better Value Healthcare Ltd

www.offoxpress.com

© J. A. Muir Gray 2011

A CIP catalogue record for this book is available from the British Library.

ISBN: 978-1-904202-07-3

Typeset by Anne Joshua, Oxford
Printed and bound in Great Britain by Information Press, Eynsham, Oxford.

Contents

CONTENTS

Preface

I do not remember when I first heard about systems, but my copy of *General System Theory: Foundations, Development, Applications* by Ludwig von Bertalanffy is inscribed '*Bought with a book token given for a talk to Oxfordshire community dietitians – 1977*'. What the talk was about I cannot remember, and neither I am sure could they, but Bertalanffy's book has had a lasting influence on me.

In 1983, in the midst of our last period of lean times, I published an article in *The Lancet* called 'Four Box Healthcare: Development in a Time of Zero Growth' (1), which proposed that all services should be planned on the basis of health problems such as '*diabetes, osteoarthritis, Parkinson's disease, menstrual disorders . . . asthma and the process of dying*'. Furthermore, with the confidence of youth, I argued that budgets should also be organised in this way because '*questions such as how shall we spend £10,000 to help people with diabetes cannot be asked*'.

Theory was put to the test when I was given responsibility for managing cervical screening in Oxfordshire, and a little later I took upon myself the responsibility of sorting out the chaos of cervical screening nationally, the latter embarked upon in part to save my own bacon. The death of a woman whose records had been mislaid by the Oxfordshire service, years before I took it on, put me at the centre of a whirlwind of blame and panic, which could be resolved only by transforming the Brownian motion that was the cervical screening service – the random movement of women, cervical smears, lab reports and professionals – into a system.

The systems approach, which has now been strongly influenced by Japanese principles, was then applied to all the national screening programmes. However, I had always wanted to apply systems thinking to health problems, such as '*menstrual disorders . . . asthma and the process of dying*', and carried out preliminary work in Oxford on the integrated population-based management of abdominal pain and people diagnosed with heart failure in collaboration with Sally Hope, Clare Parker and Richard Stephens, supported by the then Oxford Regional Health Board.

The impetus to apply systems thinking stayed with me during my work on knowledge management and information technology in the NHS, and when developing the Cochrane Collaboration with Sir Iain Chalmers and Mark Starr, which revealed the potential of the Internet to support better value healthcare.

In the end, however, it all comes down to what happens in the minds of professionals and patients, and that requires culture change. As Gandhi said:

No system can make a bad man good.

Throughout this journey, I have had the privilege to work with wonderful colleagues, and to have been supported with great forbearance by my family. The world is now moving towards a systems way of thinking. The economic crisis has provided the burning platform from which people need to jump from institutions, such as hospitals, to systems of care. Systems will be the dominant paradigm for 21st century healthcare.

J. A. Muir Gray

1

21ST CENTURY HEALTHCARE – THE SYSTEMS CENTURY

The 20th century was the century of the hospital; the 21st century is the century of the system.

The problems faced by people who pay for or manage health services in the 21st century are many and complex. Not only are resources limited, but there is a widening gap between the resources available and the need and demand for healthcare. Apart from increased need for services, service users are also changing in their attitudes, with growing consumerism leading to calls for more transparency and accountability in the planning and delivery of healthcare, and challenges to the once-dominant charismatic authority of clinicians. Furthermore, these demands and challenges are being made against a background of workforce fragmentation with high staff turnover and greater dependence on temporary staff.

From the perspective of patients, surveys reveal that they experience healthcare as chaos, or Brownian motion (see Touchstone to Chapter 2) – the random movement of patients, professionals, blood samples, images, and pieces of paper. Many patients feel they are treated as a number, and that face-to-face communication with clinicians is poor. From the perspective of clinicians, they feel time-poor while having to deal with the increasing complexity of care and a burgeoning knowledge base. They are faced with difficult decisions, having to relate the level of risk to each individual patient, in a bureaucratic health service that is governed by financial, legal and bio-ethical concerns.

Various solutions have been introduced in an attempt to solve these problems. There has been a reliance on targets, despite the repeated common response to their imposition, which is usually to fiddle the figures, fiddle the work, or fail to meet them. The intervention of the market was seen as a way of controlling healthcare costs and improving quality, but the market has not been found to have a substantial beneficial effect on health outcomes, nor has the contracting process stimulated innovation. Tougher regulation and better management have been only partly effective, and simply investing additional resources is not sustainable or feasible.

Moreover, technological and scientific advances, although important for the evolution of healthcare, are not able to solve every problem, and cannot solve the five problems found in almost every health service in the world:

- Unwarranted variation in quality and outcome;
- Harm to patients;
- Waste, and failure to maximise value;
- Health inequalities and inequities
- Failure to prevent disease.

There needs to be a more fundamental shift in the response to the problems facing healthcare in the 21st century, and the three most powerful drivers for change which are patients, new knowledge, and developments in information technology (IT).

An effective solution to the problems faced in health services is to introduce a systems approach, which has the significant advantage of not necessarily requiring structural change, and re-organisation. The development of systems thinking has spread through industry, not just manufacturing industry but a range of different industries including supplies and logistics. Influenced by Edwards Deming (1), the systems approach was famously pioneered in Japanese industry, and used to produce high-quality goods at low prices. The outcome was extremely serious for many of the competitors to Japanese companies, most notably the American car industry (2). Much of the publicity has been about Toyota production systems, partly because of the iconic figure of Taiichi Ohno (3), but every Japanese industrial sector has used systems and networks alongside their bureaucracies to improve outcomes.

Although the use of an industrial analogy for healthcare has its limitations, public services in general did not apply systems thinking and relied instead on target-setting, a failure that has been analysed by John Seddon (4).

In this book, we describe the development of systems thinking, explore the advantages of a systems approach, the problems it is able to address, and the way in which it has been applied in health services thus far.

However, in tandem with the introduction of a systems approach to the delivery of healthcare, it is important to address the culture of an organisation, a topic that is touched on in this book but dealt with in more detail in a companion volume entitled *How To Create The Right Healthcare Culture.*

The development of systems thinking (see Figure 1.1)

Descartes	Objectivism
Invention of the microscope – cells, cells, cells	Reductionism
Romanticism – Tyger! Tyger! burning bright	Holism
Brownian motion Discovery of microbes – Pasteur	Reductionism
Einstein – Nobel Prize in 1905 for the theory behind Brownian motion	Synthesis
von Bertalanffy	Systems theory

Figure 1.1 Tracing the development of systems thinking

The distinction between subjectivity and objectivity developed during the 17th century in Europe, although it is a much more recent concept in Asia. Credit for the paradigm shift that distinguished the human being from their environment is usually given to Descartes, best known for his expression 'Cogito ergo sum' ('I think, therefore I am'). The Cartesian approach implied that complex organisms, such as human beings, or environments could be subdivided into their constituent elements. Cartesianism stimulated much intellectual

3

thinking in subsequent centuries, and was particularly popular in Great Britain where people like David Hume developed the empirical tradition.

The beginnings of microscopy mirrored Descartes' lifespan, with the forerunner of the compound microscope having been built in 1590 by Zacharias and Hans Janssen, an invention that supported a reductionist view. It was not until after Descartes' death, however, that the microscope began to be used in research. In 1665, Robert Hooke observed 'pores' or cells in a slice of cork under the microscope, and in 1674 Anton van Leeuwenhoek was the first person to see bacteria.

The 18th to mid 19th centuries saw the pendulum swing back with the rise of the Romantic movement, in which poets such as Wordsworth and artists such as Turner depicted nature as something that should be appreciated in its entirety, rather than reduced to its constituent elements. To William Blake, the tiger was not a collection of tissues and organs to be further subdivided into cells, it was:

> *Tyger! Tyger! burning bright*
> *In the forests of the night*
> *What immortal hand or eye*
> *Could frame thy fearful symmetry?*

During this period, in 1827, Robert Brown first observed Brownian motion, although he did not know the cause (see Touchstone to Chapter 2), and, by the late 19th century, the pendulum had swung back again towards Reductionism. The attribution of the cause of cholera to water in 1854, based on the distribution of cholera cases around the Broad Street pump, is an excellent example of empiricism in action. John Snow's pioneering epidemiological work was highly effective in stimulating major changes in public health long before *Vibrio cholerae* and other bacteria had been identified and named. Snow's work also contributed to the germ theory of disease, which in the following decades Louis Pasteur was to confirm with his experiments on fermentation, work on parasitic infections in silkworms, and the development of vaccination for rabies.

During the early 20th century, the reductionist or mechanical conception of the world was challenged by Einstein's theory of relativity. Relativity helped to explain phenomena that could not be understood according to the laws of Newtonian physics, in which the world is composed of atoms, with each atom consisting of a nucleus surrounded by electrons in neat rings, like planets circling the sun in an 18th century orrery. Einstein's theory posited that energy, mass and light are all related, which, for many people, is incomprehensible.

Einstein's theory, however, did encourage people to take a broader or holistic view of what they saw, not in a Romantic sense, but with the understanding that a human being or an environment comprised a 'wholeness' greater than the sum of its parts. A new language evolved in the 1930s and 1940s: the term *gestalt* was used in German to describe wholeness, the word 'ecology' was introduced into environmental studies, and 'ethology', the study of human and animal development, was popularised by Konrad Lorenz (5).

From the mid 1920s through to the late 1940s, an Austrian biologist, Ludwig von Bertalanffy, had been formulating a unifying theory called general systems theory (6). In this theory, Bertalanffy described a system as 'a set of elements standing in interaction'. In addition, Bertalanffy developed a mathematical formula to describe networks, webs, and relationships, including feedback loops (positive and negative), thereby creating the foundation for the science of cybernetics (7).

For a time, Bertalanffy had been a member of the Vienna Circle, a group of philosophers, scientists and biologists who met to try to solve common problems. The Vienna Circle was highly influential, partly because of its association with Wittgenstein. The work of the Vienna Circle had a marked effect on the young A. J. Ayer whose book *Language, Truth and Logic* (8), written at the age of 24, defined the British empirical tradition for several generations.

The history of these paradigm changes is described by Fritjof Capra in *The Web of Life* (9). Capra contends that there is not a straightforward competition between reducing the world into its constituent elements on the one hand and glorying in its wholeness on the other, but that the key to understanding what happens now and in the future lies in studying the relationship between elements, as set out by Bertalanffy in his general systems theory.

The potential for systems thinking to add value to healthcare

The equations required to understand human interactions are, to use a mathematical term, non-linear. When a patient and clinician come together, the outcome is often greater than the sum of two individuals because in the 'wholeness' of the consultation things can happen that are unpredictable.

When patients and professionals are brought together to improve a service, not only is the existing service improved but also new solutions emerge (10), just as ants are able to develop solutions to problems without a hierarchy or a market (11). When the services for assessing fetal risk were coordinated using a systems approach, benefit increased and harm was reduced, both of them at lower cost, thereby increasing value.

The idea that there are at least three parties in a clinical consultation – the doctor, the patient, and the relationship between them – was first described by Michael Balint in *The Doctor, His Patient and The Illness* (12). Although the patient and doctor rarely discuss their relationship, both parties recognise that the illness is not only the link between them, but also the reason for regular consultations. Illness is what sustains the relationship (13).

Sometimes, there is another layer of complexity when patients present not only with their own problems, but also as a symptom of the problems of other people, usually family members, with whom they have a relationship. Moreover, a patient's physical problems can be compounded by psychological and social problems. Thus, clinician and patient find themselves at the centre of a web of complexity.

However, complexity can be managed, not by focusing on smaller and smaller elements of healthcare, but by looking at the problem as a whole and at the relationship between elements – this is what is meant by taking a systems approach to healthcare.

References

(1) Deming, W. E. (1986) *Out of the Crisis*. McGraw-Hill.
(2) Halberstam, D. (1986) *The Reckoning*. William Morrow & Co.
(3) Ohno, T. (1988) *Toyota Production System. Beyond Large-scale Production*. Productivity Press.
(4) Seddon, J. (2008) *Systems Thinking in the Public Sector. The failure of the reform regime . . . and a manifesto for a better way*. Triarchy Press.
(5) Lorenz, K. (1952) *King Solomon's Ring*. Routledge.
(6) von Bertalanffy, L. (1973) *General System Theory: Foundations, Development, Applications*. George Braziller Inc.
(7) Wiener, N. (1961) *Cybernetics: or Control and Communication in the Animal and the Machine*. Second edition. MIT Press.
(8) Ayer, A. J. (1936) *Language, Truth and Logic*. Victor Gollancz.
(9) Capra, F. (1997) *The Web of Life. A New Synthesis of Mind and Matter*. Flamingo.
(10) Holland, J. H. (1998) *Emergence: from chaos to order*. Perseus Books.
(11) Hölldobler, B. and Wilson, E. O. (1990) *The Ants*. Springer-Verlag.
(12) Balint, M. (1960) *The Doctor, His Patient and The Illness*. Second edition. Pitman Medical Publishing.
(13) Balint, M., Hunt, J., Joyce, D. and Marinker, M. (editors) (2001) *Treatment or Diagnosis: a study of repeat prescriptions in general practice*. Routledge.

2

WHAT IS A HEALTHCARE SYSTEM?

This chapter will:

- explain the different types of system – hard and soft, open and closed, complex;
- discuss the relationship between systems, networks, and care pathways.

By the end of the chapter you will have developed an understanding of:

- the meaning of the term 'system';
- the characteristics of different types of system;
- how systems and networks can make distinctive contributions to healthcare.

Touchstone: Healthcare as Brownian motion

The cobbler's children are aye the worst shod.

Scottish proverb

This proverb tends to be used when the son or daughter of the Manse goes off the rails. Despite this, many children of the Manse stayed firmly on the rails to make significant contributions to society, both in Scotland and abroad, their hardy upbringing having done them more good than harm.

Robert Brown was a son of the Manse, his father an Episcopalian Minister. Brown was born in Montrose in 1773, educated in Aberdeen, and later at Edinburgh University Medical School. Edinburgh at this time was a city at the heart of the Scottish enlightenment, which according to one author led to the '*invention of the modern world*' (1). Perhaps aware of Dr Johnson's adage that the best sight for a Scotsman was the high road to England, Brown began his travels in London as the ship's doctor and scientist on an expedition to Australia led by Matthew Flinders. He returned to London with a collection of botanical specimens, and became a highly respected Fellow of the Royal Society.

In 1827, Brown recorded that when studying pollen grains under the microscope he had observed particles moving within them, which he called 'Active Molecules'. This movement became known as 'Brownian motion', although Brown was unable to explain the cause. The mechanism remained unexplained for nearly 80 years until 1905 when Einstein published a theoretical analysis of Brownian motion. This was one of the three fundamental advances he made in that year, together with the concepts of spatial relativity and light quanta, developments which led to him being awarded the Nobel Prize for Physics.

Access one of the Applets on the web illustrating Brownian motion and observe the random path that any particle in a fluid follows as a result of being buffeted by 'active molecules'. Physicists describe the particle's path as a 'random walk'. Many patients experience healthcare like a particle in Brownian motion: frequent encounters with busy healthcare professionals, all operating in isolation, where each individual encounter might be useful, but the patient's progress seems random, unsystematic, and sometimes chaotic.

Defining what is meant by a 'system'

To say that a system is simply the opposite of Brownian motion is unhelpful.

A system is a set of activities with a common aim, a common set of objectives, and a set of criteria against which progress towards the objectives can be measured (see Box 2.1 for definitions of terms used throughout the book). 'Set' is a term derived from algebra, meaning a collection of entities with a common focus. Although the activities in a set can take place in different locations and in different organisations, it is possible for them to have 'a common set of objectives', in which:

- more than one activity can relate to a single objective;
- a single activity can relate to more than one objective.

In Table 2.1, the objectives of the NHS Breast Screening Programme are presented together with the activities involved.

Table 2.1: Objectives and activities of the NHS Breast Screening Programme

Objectives	Activities
<ul><li>To identify and invite eligible women for mammographic screening</li><li>To carry out mammography in a high proportion of those who were invited</li><li>To provide services that are acceptable to those who receive them</li><li>To follow up all women referred for further investigations</li><li>To minimise the adverse effects of screening – anxiety, radiation and unnecessary investigations</li><li>To diagnose cancers accurately</li><li>To support and carry out research</li><li>To make effective and efficient use of resources for the benefit of the whole population</li><li>To enable those working in the programme to develop their skills and find fulfillment in their work</li><li>To encourage the provision of effective acceptable treatment which has minimal psychological or functional side-effects</li><li>To evaluate the service regularly and provide feedback to the population served</li></ul>	<ul><li>Identifying the eligible population</li><li>Inviting women</li><li>Informing women about benefits, risks and limitations</li><li>Mammography</li><li>Biopsy and pathology of suspected cancers</li><li>Counselling and support</li><li>Treatment</li><li>Quality improvement</li></ul>

Box 2.1: Definitions of terms used throughout the book

- A system is a set of activities with a common set of objectives.
- A network is a set of organisations and individuals that deliver the system's objectives.
- A pathway is the route most patients follow through the network.
- A programme is a set of systems with a common knowledge base and a common budget; for example, within the respiratory diseases programme, there are systems for asthma and chronic obstructive pulmonary disease.

Commonalities among systems

Common to all systems are inputs, outputs, and feedback. Feedback is usually provided in the form of information. A relatively simple healthcare system is presented in Figure 2.1 showing information as feedback.

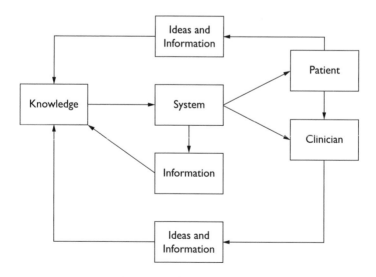

Figure 2.1 A healthcare system

Feedback information is sometimes referred to as a signal. In one of the classic books of systems literature, Oppenheim, Willsky and Nawab described the features of signals and systems, and the relationship between them:

> *Although the physical nature of the signals and systems that arise in these various disciplines [such as biomedical engineering] may be drastically different, they all have two very basic features in common. The signals, which are functions of one or more independent variables, contain information about the behavior or nature of some phenomenon, whereas the systems respond to particular signals by producing other signals or some desired behaviour.* (2)

Different types of system

Systems can be classified in many different ways. For the purposes of this book, we shall focus on only a few schemes of classification.

Open and closed systems

When considering the interaction between systems and their environment, systems can be classified into two types: open, and closed. However, these two types should not be regarded as qualitatively different; they lie at either end of a spectrum (Figure 2.2).

Figure 2.2 **The spectrum of systems from open to closed**

In a closed system, energy, but *not* matter, is exchanged with the external environment. Central heating operates as a closed system. The boiler generates heat that circulates around the house; the temperature in the room where the thermostat is situated is the signal that provides feedback to the boiler to switch it on or off. As for all closed systems, central heating is only relatively closed because not only is it influenced by the temperature outside the house but also by human behaviour, for example, someone leaving a window open.

In the human body, the system that maintains balance is similar in operation to central heating. If the body deviates from the vertical, sensors in the joints and the inner ear send a signal to the part of the brain that controls position, and corrective action is taken.

Concept applied to healthcare: Suppose a health economy is a 'closed' system: if too many patients are referred to hospital, a signal is sent to the clinic booking system, and waiting times will increase if there are no other factors influencing managerial decision-making.

In an open system, both energy *and* matter are exchanged with the external environment. Biological systems and social systems are examples of an open system. Descriptions of an open system are given in the following quotations.

> *Open systems thinking views organizations as being composed of a set of various interconnected sub-systems that together constitute the whole organization.* (3)

> *The organism is not a static system closed to the outside and always containing the identical components; it is an open system in a (quasi-) steady state . . . in which material continually enters from, and leaves into, the outside environment.* (4)

Large open systems can be difficult to control.

Concept applied to healthcare: If a hospital or health service for a population is considered as a large open system, in this type of system, a hospital's decision to let waiting times increase so that demand matches capacity could be overturned by a central political decision that there should be no increase in waiting times. Should there be a decision to increase supply to meet demand this could lead to a further increase in demand because the self-referral threshold of patients, and the referral threshold of primary care doctors, tends to be influenced by ease of access.

Hard and soft systems

Sometimes, systems can be better understood using a different pair of adjectives than 'closed' and 'open', namely, 'hard' and 'soft'. Just as the distinction between open and closed systems is one better represented by a spectrum, 'hard' and 'soft' systems represent either end of a spectrum. In a 'hard' system, there is an objective or endpoint to be achieved, and all variables are known and can be controlled. Car production lines or supermarket supply chains are sometimes characterised as 'hard' systems. In contrast, soft systems can be ill defined and not easily quantified. One of the key characteristics of a 'soft' system is that there may be competing forces within it. In a soft systems problem, there are usually several independent agencies, each intent on its own solution to the problem. For example, in an alcohol harm reduction initiative in which health educators, the police and publicans are working together, there will be tensions that have to be managed.

Systems engineering was developed to address problems associated with hard systems. John Sterman, one of the systems-thinking gurus, wrote the classic text on systems engineering, and at the Sloan School of Management, Massachusetts Institute of Technology, he trained many systems engineers (5). However, in the last decade, systems engineering has been increasingly complemented by soft systems methodology (SSM).

Soft systems methodology

Much of the pioneering work on soft systems has been done by Peter Checkland, whose ideas have been highly influential, as shown by the three quotations set out below.

> *SSM is best understood in relation to its origins. It is the problem solving approach developed from systems engineering when that approach failed. And systems engineering – impressive enough as a way of carrying out technological projects – failed when attempts were made to apply it, not to projects in the sense described above, e.g. the Great Wall of China, but to the messy, changing, ill-defined problem situations with which managers have to cope in their day-to-day professional lives. (6)*

> *Systems-based methodology for tackling real-world problems in which known-to-be-desirable ends cannot be taken as given. Soft*

systems methodology is based upon a phenomenological stance. (7)

SSM is an action-oriented process of inquiry into problematical situations in the everyday world; users learn their way from finding out about the situation to defining/taking action to improve it. The learning emerges via an organized process in which the real situation is explored, using as intellectual devices – which serve to provide structure to discussion – models of purposeful activity built to encapsulate pure, stated world-views. (8)

Checkland's classic diagram of soft systems methodology has been simplified in Figure 2.3 to show a soft systems approach.

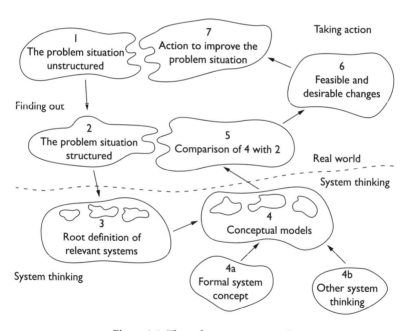

Figure 2.3 The soft systems approach

Concept applied to healthcare: Health services are often better understood in terms of hard and soft systems. The introduction of measures to reduce the amount of petrol used by a community psychiatric service appears at first sight to be a hard systems or systems engineering problem, which includes the analysis of trends, the identification of alternative solutions, the appraisal of options, and the introduction of the best-value solution. However, the actual management of the change requires a soft systems methodology because the amount of petrol used in a psychiatric service is influenced by many factors. For instance, if the qualifying criteria for a lease car include that staff must have a mileage of at least 200 miles a week, this can act to increase mileage unnecessarily, or staff may have become used to the benefits of the additional income associated with a 'regular user allowance'.

This type of problem is sometimes referred to as a 'wicked problem': one in which there are psychological as well as physical factors involved, moral as well as practical issues; a problem for which there is no right answer. Wicked problems are associated with a large amount of data, together with the need to consider social factors. Various techniques have been used to analyse wicked problems, but soft systems thinking can be helpful.

Complex systems or complex adaptive systems

Complexity theory is now widely used in systems analysis, and 'complex system', or 'complex adaptive system' as they are sometimes known, is a term in increasing use. The late Kieran Sweeney (9) identified the features of a complex system:

- sensitivity to initial conditions;
- complex responsive processes;
- self-organisation;
- adaptation (leading to co-evolution);
- emergence (see below).

Sweeney, and several other authors, have emphasised that, although complex or complex adaptive systems look daunting, there is no reason to be paralysed when having to deal with them:

1. systems are inherently complex, and it is a waste of time to wish it were otherwise;
2. the use of the term 'adaptive' is indicative – if innovation is

encouraged, human beings often adapt, and develop innovative solutions.

In his book, *Complexity: the emerging science at the edge of order and chaos*, M. Mitchell Wardrop relates how our understanding of complex adaptive systems developed. At a meeting of the best physicists and economists at the Santa Fe Institute, John H. Holland described the properties of complex adaptive systems:

> *In the natural world such systems included brains, immune systems, ecologies, cells, developing embryos, and ant colonies. In the human world they included cultural and social systems such as political parties or scientific communities. Once you learned how to recognize them, in fact, those systems were everywhere. But wherever you found them, said Holland, they all seem to share certain crucial properties.*
>
> *First, [Holland said], each of these systems is a network of many 'agents' acting in parallel.*
>
> *Furthermore, said Holland, the control of a complex adaptive system tends to be highly dispersed. There is no master neuron in the brain, for example, nor is there any master cell within a developing embryo.*
>
> *Second, said Holland, a complex adaptive system has many levels of organization, with agents at any one level serving as the building blocks for agents at a higher level. Furthermore, said Holland – and this was something he considered very important – complex adaptive systems are constantly revising and re-arranging their building blocks as they gain experience. Third, he said, all complex adaptive systems anticipate the future. Finally, said Holland, complex adaptive systems typically have many niches, each one of which can be exploited by an agent adapted to fill that niche.* (10)

Emergence

Holland developed the concept or principle of 'emergence', which he summarised as '*much coming from little*' (11).

Concept applied to healthcare: If a service has decided to improve what it offers to people with epilepsy, it could commission an academic unit or management consultant to prepare a report with recommendations. Alternatively, it could bring together people with epilepsy, their parents, carers and teachers, and professors of neurology and other experts, and consult them about their suggestions to improve the service in a context of no more resources. It is certain that this group of stakeholders would be able to identify improvements to service planning and delivery, demonstrating Holland's principle of emergence – much out of little. In the White Paper, *Equity and Excellence: Liberating the NHS* (12), there is an emphasis on how the information generated by patients will be critical to increasing the efficiency of health service provision, in what the White Paper rightly calls a 'revolution'.

Use of the term 'system' in healthcare

> *'When I use a word,' Humpty Dumpty said, in rather a scornful tone, 'it means just what I choose it to mean – neither more nor less.'*
>
> *'The question is,' said Alice, 'whether you can make words mean so many different things.'*
>
> *'The question is,' said Humpty Dumpty, 'which is to be master – that's all.'*
>
> Lewis Carroll, *Through the Looking Glass*

The term 'system' is now more widely used in healthcare than hitherto and, as it spreads, it accumulates meanings. There are several different uses of the word 'system' in healthcare:

- System as a national health service;
- System set up to deal with a health problem or single condition;
- System set up to deal with complex health problems;
- System set up to deal with a cross-cutting activity or function;
- System as a protocol.

'System' as a national health service

In 2006, the Commonwealth Fund published a report entitled *Framework for a High Performance Health System for the United States* (13).

The health system described in this report encompasses virtually everything associated with healthcare, including access to care, quality of care, and safety. A high-performance healthcare system was characterised as one that:

- has a clear national strategy;
- delivers care through models that emphasise coordination and integration;
- has a set of measures that can be used to assess health outcomes and the quality of care.

As highlighted by the Commonwealth Fund, the national level is one level at which a system can be considered. Others might have referred to a National Service for the United States of America, but the Commonwealth Fund, source of many good ideas, chose to call it a system. Thus, the term 'system' can be used to describe a whole health service, as in 'a new system of healthcare for the United States'.

An alternative term for the national level of system is a 'macro-system'; however, the terminology is fluid and 'macro-system' can also be applied to a hospital, or health economy, i.e. all the organisations serving a defined population. If 'macro-system' is applied to a hospital, the term 'meso-system' can be applied to a ward or hospital department.

'System' set up to deal with a health problem or single condition

The term 'system' can be used to describe a set of activities that focus on a health problem or single condition: for example, a system for managing rheumatoid arthritis, or screening for breast cancer. However, the term 'service' is commonly used to describe a set of activities that focus on a single condition, for instance, 'a tuberculosis service'. This interchangeability of the terms 'service' and 'system' does not necessarily matter because what defines a system is the way in which activities are coordinated rather than the use of a particular word, although interchangeability can cause confusion.

Another term that can be used as a synonym for 'system' or 'service' in this context is 'programme'. Much of the early and excellent work on the development of healthcare systems was stimulated by the

World Health Organization (WHO). The focus of the WHO on specific conditions has transformed the management of infectious diseases in many countries, for example:

- the Smallpox Eradication Programme;
- the Malaria Control Programme;
- the Onchoceriasis Control Programme.

Single disease control programmes are highly effective when managing infectious diseases.

'System' set up to deal with complex health problems

The use of the term 'system' can be used to describe a set of activities that focus on complex health and related problems, for example, a system for supporting old people with multiple health and social care problems. Complexity is a feature of many clinical and healthcare problems

'System' as a protocol

The term 'system' can be used to describe protocols for dealing with patients, such as admissions to hospital or carrying out a particular procedure; thus, a protocol is a set of activities that need to be performed to deliver an intervention, and is sometimes called a 'care bundle'. Prompts and reminders about the actions that need to be taken before carrying out a procedure can be incorporated into an electronic care pathway (see Chapter 6).

'System' set up to deal with a cross-cutting activity or function

The term 'system' can be used to describe a cross-cutting activity or function, for example, patient safety systems. Safety systems can be discussed in one of two main ways: in generic terms, for example, a 'healthcare incident reporting system', or in specific terms of systems that focus on particular types of activity, for example, a 'system for safer prescribing'.

Although the WHO has been, and continues to be, criticised for focusing on single 'vertical' programmes, the organisation has complemented this vertical approach by addressing cross-cutting themes, most notably by the commitment given to the promotion of primary care in the Alma-Ata Declaration (14).

Systems approach used in this book

Although the use of the term 'system' is appropriate in all these contexts, the systems approach described in this book is relatively simple. The focus is on systems for the management of a health problem or presentation, such as headache, or the management of a disease, such as epilepsy. Despite the danger in over-simplification, there is also a danger in over-complicating issues. Although it is true that many patients have more than one condition, it is equally true that many patients with a single condition are badly managed because of the lack of a system, thereby incurring a waste of resources and potentially harmful effects for patients.

What comprises a 'true' system in healthcare?

Calling a group of healthcare organizations a 'system' has become common practice. As Ackoff (1974, 1994) and others have noted, however, true systems involve a functionally related group of interacting, interrelated or interdependent elements forming a complex whole with a common aim. In simpler terms, systems elements must be capable of working together to achieve shared goals; otherwise, they are merely individual parts with separate missions. (15)

For every million people in England, there are about 40,000 consultations and 200,000 clinical decisions made every day. However, the healthcare offered to the population cannot be understood simply by looking at each of these consultations and decisions. The relationships between the consultations and the various services needed have to be seen as part of a system, namely, a set of activities with a common set of objectives.

To determine whether healthcare is being provided as part of a 'true' system can be answered by asking the following questions.

- Is there a clear single aim for the system?
- Is there a set of objectives?

- For each objective, has one or more criteria been chosen to measure progress?
- Are there standards against which the level of performance can be compared?
- Is there a feedback loop with information being provided that can influence the delivery of the programme? (A simple feedback loop is an annual report delivered to the population served by the system.)

Debates on healthcare often focus on primary care, hospitals or academic medical centres. In the car manufacturing industry, the corollary would be for the Board of Toyota to describe its core business as factories, service centres and showrooms, but Toyota's core business is, to quote from the website, 'Cars, Trucks, SUVs and Hybrids'.

The core business of healthcare is not hospitals or primary care; it is either groups of healthcare problems, such as mental health problems, or specific disorders such as breast cancer. Although primary care, secondary care and tertiary care were useful concepts in the past, and each needs to be well run, none of these institutions provides end-to-end care for patients. For this reason, we are focusing on systems development for health problems and conditions. This is the level at which healthcare systems should be developed. Thus, the horizontal blocks of care shown in Figure 2.4 need to be complemented by the end-to-end systems of care (the core businesses of healthcare), making a matrix as shown in Figure 2.5.

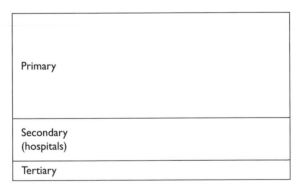

Figure 2.4 One-dimensional healthcare

	Arthritis	Epilepsy	Depression	Heart failure	Breast cancer	Asthma
Primary						
Secondary (hospitals)						
Tertiary						

Figure 2.5 Matrix showing levels of care in relation to integrated systems of care – healthcare's 'core' businesses

Networks in relation to systems

The importance of networks within systems is increasingly being recognised. Whereas a system is a set of activities with a common aim, a common set of objectives and a set of criteria against which progress towards the objectives can be measured, a *network* is a set of individuals and organisations working together to deliver the objectives of the system.

There are debates about the relationship between the terms 'network' and 'team'. Some people use the words interchangeably, but most people use the word 'team' to refer to people who work within one organisation, and the word 'network' to refer to people from different organisations who work together, for example, people working in primary and secondary care to improve mental health services.

Describing a system in terms of a set of activities can give the impression that all activities take place in parallel. However, these activities are carried out by networks. Network thinking, developed in biology, is one of the key features of systems, with the people in a network sharing thoughts and working as if they were a face-to-face team. Manuel Castells, regarded by many as the leading thinker on networks, defined a network as:

23

. . . a set of interconnected nodes. A node is a point where the network intersects itself. A network has no centre, just nodes. Nodes may be of varying relevance to the network . . . A network is defined by the program that assigns the network its goals and rules of performance. The program is made up of codes that include the valuation of performance and criteria for success or failure. (16)

It is necessary, therefore, to ensure that within a system the relationships among the different activities are clear. Systems do not by themselves deliver healthcare. That is done by the professionals who work within the system, and the patients and their carers who use it. The term 'network' in healthcare systems is usually focused on the human beings who connect with one another and relate to one another. It is essential, therefore, for a system to have a network of people. The network may consist of individuals or there may be teams at certain points within the network, for example, the multidisciplinary team (MDT) for breast cancer.

The Royal College of Paediatrics and Child Health produced clear guidance for its members on understanding pathways and implementing networks.

An individual pathway guides patients and professionals on the optimal care of individuals with a particular problem, and therefore sits within a network that will support the delivery of a number of care pathways provided by a range of professionals. (17)

As usual, there are no hard or fast definitions, and it is important when developing systems for those involved to ensure that the terms 'system' and 'network' are clearly understood, and used consistently during the development process.

Care pathways in relation to systems

A care pathway is a document that describes a process within health and social care. The document describes the journey that most patients will take through a healthcare system. The means most commonly used to display care pathways within the NHS is the

Map of Medicine®. An illustration of part of a Map or care pathway is shown in Figure 6.7.

If a system is a set of activities, the pathway is the course an individual follows as they go through the system, and at each point in the system a decision is made for the patient to follow one route or another. In breast screening, for example, all women follow the pathway up to the point where mammography is carried out; then, depending on the results of mammography, individual women will be told either that no cancer can be seen, and they are at low risk, or that they need a referral, in which case they follow another pathway through the referral process to the assessment clinic and, if necessary, on to treatment.

Pathways are particularly useful if a patient's treatment crosses institutional care boundaries, such as the boundary between primary and secondary care because neither service may be aware of the activities of the other. Documented pathways are also useful when patients have access to them because they are more likely to know at what point they are in the care pathway. Indeed, they may have more information than the clinician they are consulting, particularly if their records are missing or communication between clinicians has been imperfect. For this reason, Map of Medicine pathways are available to patients on the NHS Choices website.

The development of systems of care will inevitably lead to the development of care pathways or, to be more precise, to the expression of care pathways in documents. Although it is possible for care pathways to exist as tacit knowledge, tacit knowledge is insufficiently reliable as a basis for modern healthcare due to the high rate of staff turnover (see Chapter 3).

Programmes in relation to systems

'Programme' is a term that is often used loosely in healthcare. Recently, the word has become more familiar as part of the term 'programme budgeting', described by Mooney et al. (18) as follows:

> *The principle underlying programme budgeting is very simple. If decisions are to be made about broadly defined healthcare objectives and priorities – for example, what are the objectives*

associated with care of the elderly? What relative priorities are attached to the treatment of cancer compared with the prevention of heart disease? – then data should be provided in similarly broad terms to match the nature of the choices. (18)

However, a programme is not simply a budget. In 2010, the term 'programme' was used in the NHS to mean a set of systems with a common knowledge base and a common budget (see Box 2.1).

Organisational models: systems, bureaucracies, and markets

There are three main organisational models:

- a market – a transaction in which there is no future obligation between buyer and seller;
- a hierarchy – a system of nested groups, such as government bureaucracies, biological taxonomies or a system of menus in a software application (19);
- a network.

Over the last 50 years, debates about the relative merits and costs of the market and of the bureaucracy – or 'the firm' as a bureaucracy is described in the books and articles about industry – have swung back and forth between faith in the firm and faith in the market. More recently, networks have entered the lexicon.

Market mechanisms in healthcare

The intellectual basis for the concept of the healthcare market arose from the work of Alain Enthoven, who worked in the United States Defense Department with Robert MacNamara (20). His support for the introduction of market mechanisms into the provision of healthcare in the NHS reflected two trends.

1. The break-up of long chains of command by 'outsourcing' functions traditionally managed in-house and buying them back in to give flexibility and power to the 'purchaser'. In the car industry, when Henry Ford built the Rouge River plant, he envisaged that Ford, the company and himself, were the entity that would own

and control everything – first the panel-making, then the steel-making to produce the panels, then the iron production to make the steel, and so on. However, industry subsequently saw advantages in focusing the efforts of managers and workers on the jobs they did best – 'Stick to the knitting' was the slogan in the 1980s' best seller *In Search of Excellence* (21) – while stimulating competition between suppliers, which led to the development of the market.

2. The choice of the market as a means of improving healthcare in the 1980s, which was not made solely on business grounds. It was also political, namely, to initiate or accelerate change in a venerable but, as perceived by the Conservative Party, stagnant British institution. The professionals who said they were concerned with the stability of the NHS at this time were seen as reactionary. The Labour Party, when it took office in 1996, changed the language in use, and removed some features of the market, such as the concentration on short-term 'spot transactions'. However, they kept the functional split between the definition of need and allocation of resources on one hand, and the provision of services on the other.

Faith in the market, at least in the pure and undiluted form, began to wane for several reasons:

- as a result of experience;
- because of intellectual challenges, notably expressed by Thomas Rice:

    Other texts generally accept that, unless there is strong evidence to the contrary, relying on market competition will result in best outcomes – at least with respect to efficiency . . . this book has taken (and justified, we hope) an entirely different approach . . . we have examined over a dozen of the assumptions that would need to be fulfilled to ensure that a free market results in the best outcome for society; we found none of them even close to being met in health . . . economic theory provides no basis for assuming the superiority of competitive approaches. (22)

- the way in which markets worked in effective economies; in Japan, during its most successful period of economic growth, a variant on the pure market developed together with a way of working in which management focused more on growth than on control.

When some services or the production of some components were externalised in the United Kingdom, the fashion in the pure market was for the contractor and the supplier to work at arms-length, to stay distant from one another so that no 'cosy' relationships developed. The focus was on the 'spot' transaction, and the contract was seen to express the power of the customer. The fear of losing the contract was deemed sufficient to control the contractor, such that they would behave as the customer wished. However, this type of market dominated by the 'spot' transaction did not encourage innovation.

By comparison, in Japan, much longer relationships were developed between the company providing components and the main assembly company. The two companies, supplier and contractor, would work closely together, with exchange visits where workers would discuss requirements and processes, exchange ideas, and, even more important, generate ideas for cost-cutting and quality improvement. The network of companies around a large car company such as Toyota or Nissan was called a *keiretsu*, and although the companies were all independent the big player was the dominant force. Nonetheless, a genuine collaboration existed between the two firms, codified in the contract which recognised the need for collaborative working if both parties were to benefit.

On the production floor, the principle of collaboration was also one of the reasons why Japanese companies could achieve year-on-year quality improvement. Large Japanese companies became what are now known as learning organisations. Workers at all levels were generating ideas for quality improvement, which were treated with equal respect irrespective of source, and team-working was encouraged with groups of workers collaborating with each other (23). The collaborative nature of the Japanese production company was reinforced by the social ties engendered by lifelong employment and the concept of the company as a family.

There is evidence that competition, even within the public sector, can stimulate innovation. Research suggests that hospitals which competed '*took steps to improve their efficiency without compromising patient care or excluding high-risk patients*'. (24) Bureaucracies can inhibit innovation through their sheer size or because in the public sector they must follow strict rules and procedures when investing public money in new ventures. It can take a year or more for an innovation to be funded if a bureaucracy has to follow European Union regulations.

However, even markets are hindered by regulation, and increasingly so. This phenomenon was first highlighted by Michael Power in *The Audit Society* (25), in which he describes how each contract let in the interests of efficiency actually entails costs through writing specifications, procurement processes, contracting, and audit. This process increasingly incurs substantial lawyers' fees. Power's perspective is gaining universal acceptance as epitomised by the award in 2009 of the Nobel Prize for Economics to two economists who challenged conventional wisdom. Oliver Williamson, one of the Nobel laureates, was the author of a devastating critique of 'transaction costs'. (26)

It is now recognised that collaboration is possible between competitors, sometimes referred to as 'co-opetition'. A group of competing organisations can invest in developing an innovation together, for example, a new technology or novel audit systems. Each organisation can then use the innovation to carry out their business, including competing with the other organisations that were involved in developing the innovation.

Furthermore, systems can and, some argue (27), must compete with one another, either for more business or to become the best, or both.

The collaborative century

If the 20th century was dominated by bureaucracies and markets, the 21st century will be dominated by collaboratives, cooperatives, networks or complex adaptive systems – the names vary but the principle is the same. Individuals and agencies cooperate to achieve common goals. In the pure version of the market, payers and providers perform different functions (see Figure 2.6).

| People who pay for health services, payers, focus on equity, allocative efficiency and value | Contract | People who provide health services, providers, focus on patient experience, technical efficiency and quality |

Figure 2.6 Market separation of people who pay for and people who provide health services

In the approach recommended in the White Paper, *Equity and Excellence: Liberating the NHS* (12), the need for partnership was explicitly emphasised with commissioners (or payers) and providers working together (see Figure 2.7).

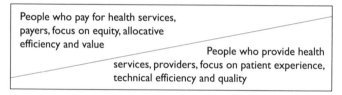

Figure 2.7 Partnership between people who pay for and people who provide health services

In management theory, such arrangements might be classified as a complex adaptive system. In biology, the example of ants is increasingly being used, in part due to the influence of E. O. Wilson. Ants operate neither by command and control or through the market; they work together, learn together, and are very successful, and some of their behaviours can be described as altruistic. (28)

Examples of systems in healthcare

A systems approach has been adopted in healthcare:

- To run screening programmes;
- For the management of certain conditions;
- To improve quality and value.

In most countries, screening programmes are managed as population-based systems, and increasingly this is the case for certain chronic diseases such as cancer.

The NHS Breast Screening Programme

Screening programmes are relatively simple systems towards the 'closed' end of the spectrum (see Figure 2.2):

- The population in need, that is, the target population, is defined explicitly, for example, pregnant women or men older than 65 years;
- The intervention is standardised – clinicians conform to this standardisation because they know they are dealing with a healthy population some members of which will be harmed even though they do not have the disease for which they are being screened (see Fig. 2.8).

	Disease present	Disease absent
No harm from screening		
Harm from screening		

Figure 2.8 The screening 'contract' – some people who do not have any chance of benefit will be harmed

The objectives and activities of the NHS Breast Screening Programme are shown in Table 2.1. Some of the objectives relate to more than one activity, and some of the activities relate to more than one objective, but:

- there is no objective that does not have at least one related activity; and
- there is no activity that does not have at least one objective.

In this example, the term 'programme' is a synonym for 'service' or 'system'.

Conditions managed on a population basis

A systems approach has been adopted for some conditions. However, there are different drivers for the adoption of a systems approach. For instance, the control of infectious diseases is managed using a systems approach because of a culture that emphasises the need to consider populations as well as affected individuals.

By contrast, although in many countries cancer, heart disease, end-stage renal failure, and acute stroke are now managed through systems, the drivers for change have been technical rather than cultural. In the management of acute stroke, for instance, the recognition of the need for early diagnosis and intervention was created by developments in interventional radiology, which then made it necessary for systems to be set up that not only ensured people with stroke were assessed within 24 hours but also minimised capital investment by focusing the population on a small number of neuro-imaging facilities.

For those conditions where there has not been a technological driver, progress in setting up systems of care has been slower, but interest is increasing, particularly in the United States of America where a new type of organisation known as the accountable care organisation (ACO) is being promoted and developed.

The ACO model is based on 3 design principles: accountability of the ACO for the entire continuum of care for a defined population of patients; payment reforms that reward quality improvement and slow spending increases while avoiding excessive financial risk for the ACOs; and reliable performance measurement to support improvement and provide public confidence that lower cost can be achieved with better care. (29)

Thus, a new language is developing to describe a new type of healthcare organisation, especially as the language needs to encompass not only the system itself but also the governance and accountability of the system. The language varies from one country to another. In England, some people use the term 'pathway hub'; in the Netherlands, the term 'care groups' is used; in the United States of America not only is the term 'accountable care organization' being used but also, owing to Michael Porter's influence, other terms such as 'integrated care delivery network' and 'integrated practice network'.

Clinical microsystems to improve quality and value

Bureaucracies and systems are not incompatible. Bureaucracies can work together within a system – a screening system or a cancer management system, for example – but clinical systems can also exist within a bureaucracy like a large hospital.

A large hospital is one of the landmark institutions of the 20th century. Like secular cathedrals, they were erected in every town and city, with the same battery of signs directing people to services: 'Gastroenterology', 'Imaging', 'Biochemistry' and 'Physiotherapy'. All too often, these departments work in isolation, and sometimes in competition. Indeed, recently, the remark was made that a modern hospital is simply a set of departments united only by complaints about car parking.

However, the Institute of Healthcare Improvement (IHI) introduced the need for systems thinking to improve both the quality and safety of healthcare. One team based in Dartmouth developed what they called a clinical microsystem approach:

> *Health care is the concern of small units and large health systems, of microsystems and macroorganizations. Our primary focus is on the* sharp end *of care – the places where care is actually delivered in the real world. We call these small frontline systems of care* clinical microsystems. *They are, literally, the places where patients and families and careteams meet.* (30)

The distinction between a clinical microsystem and an accountable care organisation appears to be well defined when described by their leading exponents. However, in practice, the distinction is not always so obvious because complexity requires a collaborative approach.

Furthermore, it is interesting to note that as the emphasis shifts from quality improvement, at whatever the cost, to increased value (i.e. the relationship between outcome and cost), systems are perceived as the means of achieving the latter as well as the former. In the most recent publication from the Dartmouth team, *Value by Design. Developing Clinical Microsystems to Achieve Organizational Excellence,* the 'bottom line' is that quality is made by the local system at points in time, whereas value is created by the whole system over time. (31)

Systems are more intelligent than bureaucracies or markets.

Questions for reflection or for use in network building or teaching

If using these questions during network building or teaching, ask the group to work in pairs on each question for three minutes; try to get people who do not know one another to work together.

When taking feedback, let each pair make only one point. In the interests of equity, if you start with the pair on the left-hand side of the room for the first question, start with the pair on the right-hand side of the room for the second question.

- If you were to score systems from 0, indicating Brownian motion, to 100, the best organised, what score would you give your service for:
  - rheumatoid arthritis;
  - childhood leukaemia;
  - end-stage renal disease;
  - epilepsy?
- Which of the clinical networks you know of works best, and why do you think it works so well?
- What are the principal barriers to the creation of systems in the healthcare sector?

References

(1) Herman, A. (2003) *The Scottish Enlightenment. The Scots' Invention of the Modern World.* Fourth Estate.

(2) Oppenheim, A. V. and Willsky, A. S. with Nawab, S. H. (1996) *Signals & Systems.* Second edition. Pearson.

(3) Alvesson, M. and Sveningsson, S. (2007) *Changing Organizational Culture. Cultural change work in progress.* Routledge.

(4) Capra, F. (1997) *The Web of Life. A New Synthesis of Mind and Matter.* Flamingo.

(5) Sterman, J. (2000) *Business Dynamics. Systems Thinking and Modeling for a Complex World.* McGraw-Hill.

(6) Rosenhead, J. and Mingers, J. (editors) (2001) *Rational Analysis for a Problematic World Revisited. Problem structuring methods for complexity, uncertainty and conflict.* Second edition. John Wiley & Sons.

(7) Checkland, P. (1999) *Systems Thinking, Systems Practice.* [Includes a 30-year retrospective.] John Wiley & Sons.

(8) Checkland, P. and Poulter, J. (2006) *Learning for Action. A Short Definitive Account of Soft Systems Methodology and its use for Practitioners, Teachers and Students.* John Wiley & Sons.

(9) Sweeney, K. (2006) *Complexity in Primary Care: understanding its value.* Radcliffe Publishing Ltd.

(10) Wardrop, M. M. (1992) *Complexity: the Emerging Science at the Edge of Order and Chaos.* Penguin Books Ltd.

(11) Holland, J. H. (1998) *Emergence, from Chaos to Order.* Perseus Books

(12) Department of Health (2010) *Equity and Excellence: Liberating the NHS.* Available at: http://www.dh.gov.uk/en/Publicationsand statistics/Publications/PublicationsPolicyAndGuidance/DH_117353

(13) The Commonwealth Fund Commission on a High Performance Health System (2006) *Framework for a High Performance Health System for the United States.* Commonwealth Fund Publication 943. Available at: http://www.commonwealthfund.org/Content/Publications/Fund-Reports/2006/Aug/Framework-for-a-High-Performance-Health-System-for-the-United-States.aspx

(14) World Health Organization (1978) *Declaration of Alma-Ata.* International Conference on Primary Health Care, Alma-Ata, USSR, 6–12 September 1978. Available at: http://www.who.int/hpr/NPH/docs/declaration_almaata.pdf

(15) Baker, G. R., Macintosh-Murray, A., Porcellato, C., Dionne, L., Stelmacovich, K. and Born, K. (2008) *High Performing Healthcare Systems. Delivering Quality by Design. An examination of leadership strategies, organizational processes and investments made to create and sustain improvement in healthcare.* Longwoods Publishing Corporation.

(16) Castells, M. (editor) (2004) *The Network Society. A Cross-cultural Perspective.* Edward Elgar Publishing Ltd.

(17) Royal College of Paediatrics and Child Health (2006) *A guide to understanding pathways and implementing networks.* December 2006. Available at: http://www.rcpch.ac.uk/sites/default/files/Guide%20to %20Understanding%20Pathways%20and%20Implementing %20Networks.pdf

(18) Mooney, G. H., Russell, E. M. and Weir, R. D. (1980) *Choices for Health Care.* The Macmillan Press Ltd.

(19) Wright, A. (2007) *Glut. Mastering information through the ages.* Joseph Henry Press, Washington DC.

(20) Enthoven, A. C. (1980) *Health Plan. The Only Practical Solution to the Soaring Cost of Medical Care.* Addison Wesley Publishing Co.

(21) Peters, T. and Waterman, R. H. (1995) *In Search of Excellence: Lessons from America's Best-Run Companies.* HarperCollins.

(22) Rice, T. H. (1998) *The Economics of Health Reconsidered.* Health Administration Press.

(23) Nonaka, I. and Takeuchi, H. (1995) *The Knowledge-Creating Company: How Japanese Companies Create the Dynamics of Innovation.* Seventh edition. Oxford University Press, USA.

(24) Cooper, Z., Gibbons, S., Jones, S. and McGuire, A. (2010) *Does Hospital Competition Improve Efficiency? An Analysis of the Recent Market-Based Reforms to the English NHS.* CEP Discussion Paper No 988. Centre for Economic Performance. London School for Economics and Political Science. Available at: http://eprints.lse.ac.uk/28578/1/dp0988.pdf

(25) Power, M. (1997) *The Audit Society: Rituals of Verification.* Oxford University Press, Oxford.

(26) Williamson, O. E. and Masten, S. E. (editors) (1999) *The Economics of Transaction Costs.* Edward Elgar Publishing Ltd.

(27) Porter, M. E. and Teisberg, E. O. (2006) *Redefining Health Care: Creating Value-Based Competition on Results.* Harvard Business School Press.

(28) Hölldobler, B. and Wilson, E. O. (1990) *The Ants.* Springer-Verlag.

(29) Shortell, S. M. and Casalino, L. P. (2010) Implementing Qualifications Criteria and Technical Assistance for Accountable Care Organizations. *JAMA* 303:1747–1748. doi: 10.1001/jama.2010.575

(30) Nelson, E. C., Batalden, P. B. and Godfrey, M. M. (2007) *Quality by Design. A Clinical Microsystems Approach.* Jossey-Bass.

(31) Nelson, E. C., Batalden, P. B., Godfrey, M. M. and Lazar, J. S. (2011) *Value by Design. Developing Clinical Microsystems to Achieve Organizational Excellence.* Jossey-Bass.

3

WHY IS A SYSTEMS APPROACH TO HEALTHCARE ESSENTIAL?

This chapter will:

- describe the problems common to all health services that cannot be solved by greater investment or scientific advances;
- summarise the principal challenges of 21st century healthcare;
- describe the limitations of health service re-organisation and structural change.

By the end of the chapter you will have developed an understanding of:

- the problems that plague health services, and how systems can mitigate them;
- the trends in modern healthcare that increase the need for systems;
- the contribution that systems can make to improving good outcomes, reducing poor outcomes, and minimising cost.

Touchstone:
The health service as a square peg in a round hole

You can't put a square peg into a round hole.
English language idiom

The expression 'You can't put a square peg in a round hole' has been in use in the English language for at least 200 years. Traditionally, it is used to refer to someone who does not fit in or feels out of place particularly in a job or an organisation.

However, when considering the problems and challenges that face healthcare in the 21st century in relation to the 'solutions' that have been put in place during the 20th century, it is fair to say that the 20th century configuration, planning and delivery of health services will not be appropriate in the 21st century – it would be like trying to put a square peg in a round hole. Thus, neither more nor less of the same is the answer.

More of the same is not the answer because more money is not available. Even if it were, it would not be appropriate to spend it on yet more bureaucracy to administer the pattern of facilities and professions that have been built up over the last 100 years.

Less of the same is not the answer because all organisations, businesses and industries will have to reduce their carbon footprint drastically.

What is needed is transformation, a new paradigm, and that is what systems offer.

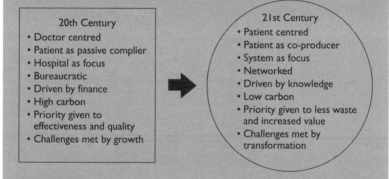

Figure 3.1 A new healthcare paradigm for the 21st century

Problems and challenges in 21st century healthcare

The last 50 years have seen remarkable progress in healthcare. Scientific advances, combined with the investment of large amounts of money and good management, have increased not only people's life-expectancy but also their years of life free from disability. However, many healthcare problems persist, problems that beset every society irrespective of the type of health service provided, whether it is tax- or insurance-based, public or private. The five main problems in 21st century healthcare are:

- Unwarranted variation in quality and outcome;
- Harm to patients;
- Waste, and failure to maximise value
- Health inequalities and inequities;
- Failure to prevent disease.

During the next 25 years, those who pay for or provide health services will have to take action to address not only these problems, but also the three main challenges of modern healthcare:

- Increasing need;
- Rising demand;
- Limited resources, no additional money, and increasing restrictions on the use of carbon.

The interventions that have been employed hitherto in the health services of different countries to mitigate the impact of these problems and challenges are similar, and include:

- Greater investment in research;
- Increased levels of regulation;
- Repeated structural re-organisation;
- Increasingly intensive and expensive professional education;
- Repeated changes in health-service financing, including the introduction of pay for performance.

Despite the common approach worldwide, the effectiveness of these interventions has been limited. In particular, the preoccupation with structural change, and the introduction of financial incentives and penalties, have been unrewarding.

Interventions to address the problems and challenges of 21st century healthcare need to have as their focus more than just the structures of health services; the focus needs to be on people and systems, and the culture in which both operate. Effective solutions require the introduction and establishment of systems, but must also take into account the culture, beliefs and attitudes of patients, clinicians, and the people who pay for healthcare. This type of approach has had greater success than solely structural approaches, as evidenced by the work of the Institute of Healthcare Improvement in the United States of America. Using systems allows the people who pay for or manage healthcare to derive the maximum value from the available resources, whether the resource is money, carbon, and/or the time of healthcare professionals and patients. The benefits of systems are shown in Box 3.1.

Box 3.1 The benefits of systems

- Resource allocation is made more explicit
- The effects of complexity, social diversity, staff turnover, and the knowledge explosion are mitigated
- Harm to patients is reduced by improving quality and reducing errors
- Unwarranted variation in activity, quality and outcome is made explicit, leading to action to reduce it
- The right patients are seen by the right service
- The unnecessary use of resources is minimised
- Inequality and inequity are made obvious, leading to action to reduce them
- Disease prevention is facilitated
- The complexity of healthcare is reduced through the process of standardisation, and chaos is transformed into order
- The institutional memory of a stable workforce is incorporated, and made available to a transient workforce

---

Culture can be changed, and systems created, by harnessing what Manuel Castells has called the three drivers of the Third Industrial Revolution: citizens, knowledge, and the Internet (1). Although

Castells specialises in writing about the industrial revolution, his ideas are equally relevant to healthcare. The comprehensive approaches needed to address the problems and challenges of 21st century healthcare are different from the solutions applied during the 20th century, such as regulation and professional education. Although these specific interventions continue to be needed, they are not sufficient, not only because they failed to prevent the five major problems found in almost every health service but also because they are unable to counteract four trends that have increased the difficulties associated with delivering health services in the 21st century.

1. The social context is more diverse;
2. Care is more complex;
3. The health service workforce is more fragmented;
4. The volume of knowledge is growing dramatically.

Although these trends do not represent direct challenges to healthcare provision in the way that increasing need, rising demand and limited resources do, they do increase the difficulties associated with the management and delivery of healthcare.

A systems approach to coping with diversity

The provision of healthcare is not an island, entire of itself; it is a service both for and operating within society. However, most societies are becoming more diverse due to several fundamental social shifts.

- The ethical shift – decisions that were once considered simple, and made without explicit discussion, are now made in the open with the potential for conflict or confusion;
- The legal shift – new laws and regulations are often introduced without a commensurate reduction in existing legislation or regulation;
- The socio-demographic shift – the ethnic mix of many populations is changing, for instance, services for older people in the United Kingdom now need to support people from many different cultures and ethnic backgrounds.

These societal shifts require those who manage care to be more open and explicit about the process of care. The use of systems as the principal type of organisation, rather than institutions, enables this transparency. One example of this would be that any antenatal screening programme needs to take into account the range of attitudes towards termination expressed by different cultures and religions, and ensure that the right option is offered to each individual woman and her partner.

A systems approach to coping with complexity

Over the last 40 years, the clinical care of an individual patient has become more complicated, because there are a greater number of diagnostic and treatment options (see Display 3.1).

Display 3.1

Once upon a time, the administration of a drug meant...	*Once upon a time, the management of a seriously ill patient meant...*
• Setting up a drip • Injecting the drug into a bag of saline solution	• Monitoring respiration, pulse rate and blood pressure • Noting the measurements on a chart
Nowadays...	Nowadays...
• Drugs are administered using infusion pumps	• Seriously ill patients are continuously monitored by machines measuring these and many other variables

The more complicated care becomes, the greater the likelihood of errors.

Systems can mitigate the impact of more complicated processes through introducing standardisation. The verb 'to standardise' is used to describe the series of actions or operations involved in defining the process most likely to produce a good result, and to provide a platform for doing better in the future.

To standardize something – whether it was a nomenclature, a product, or a procedure, or the setting of a minimal expected performance – made it more effective and more efficient. It linked the object of these efforts and those undertaking the efforts strongly to the realms of science and technology, in whose progress managers and health care professionals, patients and community leaders all strongly believed. (2)

Although 'cookbook' medicine has been criticised and derided, particularly in the early days of evidence-based medicine, cookbooks are essential to make certain dishes. Almost anyone is capable of making vegetable soup without a cookbook, but a cookbook is critical for making a soufflé or marmalade, especially if it is for the first time, not only for the list and proportion of ingredients, but also for the sequence of actions and to produce the optimum environment for a successful outcome. The standardisation of processes in healthcare, sometimes called microsystems or care bundles, simplifies care, particularly for the inexperienced clinician, without sacrificing effectiveness.

Objections to standardisation sometimes have their origin in the consequences of standardisation, and not the process itself.

standardization is a thoroughly political enterprise in at least two ways. First of all, standardization is political in the sense that the process of standardization is typified by ongoing negotiations between a host of actors, none of whom is in control or oversees all issues that may be at stake. . . . Second, standardization is political since it inevitably reorders practices, and such reorderings have consequences that affect the position of actors (through, for example, the distribution of resources and responsibilities). (2)

Not only has the care of the individual become more complicated, the care for populations has become more complex. Although there are different definitions of the term complexity, it is obvious that the planning and delivery of health services is complex, as highlighted by the following statement of Whittaker's.

A precise measure of systemic complexity has been proposed as variety, meaning the number of distinguishable elements in a system, or by extension the number of distinguishable systemic states. (3)

43

It is important to emphasise that complexity is different from chaos:

Chaos theory is not the same as complexity, and it is helpful to distinguish between the two, particularly in relation to social systems. Chaos theory describes non-linear dynamics based on the iteration of mathematical formulae which, as we have seen with the modelling of biological populations, can give rise to unpredictable behaviour and the intricate patterning of fractals.

However, it is within the repeated iteration of the constant formula that the inherent difference between chaotic and complex systems lies. Complex systems may be capable of adapting and evolving, and of changing the rules of their interaction – for example, in relation to a major change in their environment. They are not created simply by the iterative application of a formula. (4)

The reason it is important to distinguish between complexity and chaos is that complexity can be managed whereas chaos cannot. However, as complexity increases, so do the difficulties associated with managing it. The introduction of systems can reduce complexity and *transform* chaos into order.

Before the development of the NHS Cervical Screening Programme, there was chaos. Even if some of the activities such as the taking of a smear and its examination were done well, the sum of all the activity was simply three million tests being undertaken every year. No-one knew how well one service was doing in comparison with another, or whether the performance of an individual service was improving or worsening. However, as the screening programme developed a systematic approach (see Figure 3.2), order began to emerge, and could be tracked in the annual reports of the NHS Cervical Screening Programme.

A systems approach to coping with a fragmented workforce

The consultants in the unit, all male, are not against women, just against motherhood. They say the service won't work with part-time staff, but they have to realise that everything needs to change; they are not there all the time. In future, it should be assumed that everyone is part-time.

A female specialist registrar

That bloody health centre. They used to have four full-time GPs; they now have twelve, all part-time. They haven't a clue what to refer.

A hospital consultant

There used to be one rheumatologist, now there are seven. I don't know what they all get up to.

A general practitioner

Decades ago, the collective memory of a primary care or hospital team was relatively easy to express, and capture in one photograph (see Display 3.2).

Objectives	Criteria	Standards		Present position	Targets
		Minimal	Achievable		
To cover the population who would benefit from cervical screening	Percentage of women who have *not* had a hysterectomy who have had a readable smear in the last 5 years	50%	80%	70 general practices at less than 50% coverage 17 general practices at greater than 80% coverage	By the end of the year: 1 out of 70 general practices at less than 70% 35 general practices at greater than 80% coverage

Figure 3.2 Standards incorporated into an integrated system of care for cervical screening

45

Display 3.2

Once upon a time in primary care . . .	Once upon a time in hospitals . . .

• There were two or three general practitioners (GPs) to a practice
• There was a small number of support staff
• Each GP had been in practice 20–30 years and knew many of their patients well
	• The number of consultants was relatively small – three or four per hospital
	• There was one clearly defined Chief
	• Each consultant ran a 'firm' with their own ward
	• Junior doctors or doctors in training worked 100 or more hours a week and tended not to have problems – apart from fatigue – due to the relatively small number of hand-overs
	• Each ward sister:
	  – Had worked on the ward for years or decades
	  – Acted as the ward's memory
	  – With little chance of promotion to matron, held a key role
	  – Educated nurses, medical students, junior doctors and even consultants about the ward and the clinical practice that took place there

Display 3.3

Once upon a time . . .	Once upon a time . . .
• The hospital was conceived as 'A Hospital with a View' – each of the 300 hospitals in England provided almost all the care needed for the patients referred by general practitioners practising within sight of the hospital, a population of ~200,000–300,000 • Teaching hospitals were developed to house among others the specialties that required a population of 2,000,000–3,000,000	• Hospitals were staffed using the Noah's Ark principle • Specialists were employed 'two by two' to ensure cover • Colleagues from other specialties, but with training in general medicine or general surgery, provided back-up when one of the specialists was away

Consider the position in the health service now:

- ward sisters leave, or get promoted into a wider range of jobs, and therefore stay for a much shorter period of time on a ward;
- many wards house patients from many 'firms', militating against the development of corporate memory;
- junior doctors work fewer hours; in many wards, there are now up to three handovers a day instead of one, two or none;
- in some parts of the country, for several services, but particularly mental health, locum, part-time or agency staff make up a significant proportion of the clinical team.

Contrast this with the position of the health services at the inception of the NHS in 1948 (see Display 3.3). One of the major benefits of introducing systems into healthcare is that they are able to incorporate the institutional memory of a stable workforce, and make it available to a transient workforce.

A systems approach to coping with growth in the volume of knowledge

Knowledge is one resource that is in plentiful supply. The application of what we already know will have a greater impact on health and disease than any new drug or technology likely to be discovered in the next 50 years. Knowledge is the enemy of disease.

Until recently, the amount of knowledge required by a specialist was relatively limited, but there has been a steady increase in the production of high-quality evidence, combined with an increased emphasis on the importance of evidence in health-service decision-making, i.e. getting knowledge into action.

In the past, we sought to get knowledge into action by educating clinicians, and, more recently, by educating patients, but the introduction of a systems approach offers a much more reliable route for getting knowledge into action.

In health services, information is one of the three types of generalisable knowledge (see Figure 3.3):

- knowledge from research, sometimes called evidence;

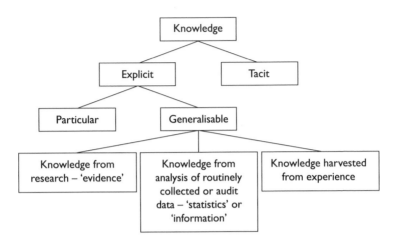

Figure 3.3 Types of knowledge

- knowledge from the analysis of routinely collected or audit data sometimes called statistics;
- knowledge from experience, which needs to be made explicit using techniques such as knowledge harvesting in which a person retiring or leaving an organisation is interviewed to capture the knowledge their successor will need.

Systems express tacit knowledge; they allow experience to be captured, and create a context in which inexperienced clinicians can make better decisions and feel less stressed. Systems can also incorporate and implement new knowledge.

Over the last six decades, there has been an enormous growth in the volume of new knowledge (see Display 3.4).

A system for managing knowledge is vital. Any knowledge management system should have a clear set of objectives, with one person on the senior management team given explicit responsibility for ensuring that:

- the organisation is able to acquire the knowledge it needs;
- the knowledge is organised, and disseminated to those who need it;
- the knowledge produced by the organisation, such as patient information, is of high quality.

Display 3.4

Once upon a time, when the body of clinical knowledge was small, all that was needed was ...	*The advantages of a small body of clinical knowledge ...*
• a single textbook encapsulating the relevant knowledge for a specialty • the British National Formulary • a local hospital formulary or handbook	• Management and dissemination of knowledge was easy • All clinicians in a health service used the same evidence base
Nowadays, with the growth in new knowledge and the development of the Internet ...	**The advantages and corresponding disadvantages of the growth in new knowledge and development of the Internet are ...**

• Best current knowledge can be made available:
  – everywhere;
  – on a variety of platforms
	• Dissemination of new knowledge can be rapid but uneven
	• All clinicians in a health service may not be using the same evidence base
	• There may be confusion about what is the best available knowledge

The person entrusted with this responsibility is the Chief Knowledge Officer. The Chief Knowledge Officer needs support, entailing a change in the role of librarian from that of custodian of bookstacks to manger of knowledge. A companion volume, entitled *How To Manage Knowledge In A Health Service*, will deal with these and other issues in more depth.

How systems reduce the five major problems in all health services

The development of systems is one of the main ways in which the five major problems of 21st century healthcare can be addressed. As stated earlier, the five major problems are:

• Unwarranted variation in quality and outcome;
• Harm to patients;
• Waste, and failure to maximise value;

- Health inequalities and inequities;
- Failure to prevent disease.

How systems can reduce unwarranted variation in quality and outcome

Although the focus on quality that has dominated healthcare for the last decade has been welcome, it is now recognised that despite the fact that quality determines outcome it is better to focus on outcome. If outcome cannot be measured, or will take too long to become evident, as is the case with breast cancer mortality when used as the outcome measure for breast screening, then quality measures of the process of care have to be used.

If quality is defined as the degree to which a service conforms to pre-set standards of goodness, it must follow that a service without standards is one unable to improve its quality. Standard-setting requires the existence of a system with objectives, and criteria that can be used to measure performance against standards. For the quality of healthcare to be improved, a systems approach is necessary.

The use of systems to improve quality has received the most publicity when compared with the level of publicity about the other benefits of systems, especially given the excellent literature on Japanese industry (5) and about Toyota in particular (6). There are even publications about the application of Toyota principles and practice to healthcare (7), which remains relevant even after Toyota's recent problems in 2009 and 2010.

There are two ways in which systems can improve healthcare quality:

- by helping individuals do better;
- by helping organisations do better.

Helping individuals do better

Consultations and clinical decisions lie at the heart of the healthcare process. They determine clinical outcome, the patient's experience of care, and the use of resources. Interventions to improve the performance of individuals vary widely, but can be classified into three types:

- educational interventions, designed to improve knowledge and skill;
- motivational interventions, designed to improve performance;
- regulatory interventions, designed to detect and prevent poor performance.

All three types of interventions have the individual professional as a focus. However, to concentrate on competence and motivation alone is to overlook the fact that for many professionals the principal determinant of poor performance is the barriers they face (see Box 3.2) rather than incompetence or lack of motivation. This relationship has been encapsulated in a formula by workers at McMaster University.

$$\text{Performance} \int \frac{\text{Competence} \times \text{Motivation}}{\text{Barriers}}$$

$$\text{P} \int \frac{\text{C} \times \text{M}}{\text{B}}$$

Many of the barriers faced by an individual cannot be overcome by an individual, no matter how resourceful they might be.

Box 3.2 Barriers to good performance

- Lack of time
- Insufficient computer terminals to access evidence easily on the ward
- Lost records
- Missing data, for example, laboratory test results

Interventions that focus on the individual alone are of limited effectiveness for the reason that individuals work in context and, increasingly, in teams in one organisation or in networks across organisations. Interventions to help individuals improve need to be complemented by interventions to help organisations improve.

Helping organisations do better

In the end, an organisation does better only if the individuals who work within it do better. This has been demonstrated in the three most convincing studies of successful organisation – *In Search of Excellence* (8), the book of the 1980s, *Built to Last* (9), the book of the 1990s, and *Good to Great* (10), published in 2001. These books do not contain a single organogram, neither do they include job descriptions of directors of strategy or chief executives. The picture they paint is of communities of people committed to working together for a common goal, often in loosely defined and fluid teams.

It is interesting to note that charismatic leadership was not identified as a critical success factor, at least not charismatic in the sense of flamboyant and extrovert. Although leadership is important, it is Factor 5 leadership, to use Jim Collins' term, that is critical, i.e. not '*a genius with a thousand followers*' but someone who enables everyone to flourish (10). This requires any leader to focus on what Peters and Waterman (8) called the 'soft stuff', especially culture. The more challenging the context, the greater the need to support and enable the staff in the frontline. The job of the organisation is discharged through the people who work for it and, in the case of a health service, by those who are served by it. The structure is relatively unimportant, but individuals need a framework, and that framework is provided by systems.

Even when an organisation has the right culture, i.e. patient-centred and focused on outcomes, it cannot deliver good-quality care or higher value without systems, some of which will focus on the mission – cancer or mental health, for example – others of which will focus on the functional units that provide support for frontline staff – systems for ordering supplies or managing finance, for example. Both types of system are needed, but most healthcare organisations have concentrated on the latter, and ignored the former. Healthcare organisations, like many other types of organisation, are hybrid organisations. As Andy Grove, creator of Intel, has pointed out, in hybrid organisations '*functional units and mission-orientated units work together, with the accompanying principle of dual reporting*'. Grove goes on to say that hybrid organisations '*are not great in and of themselves they just happen to be the best way for any business to be organised*'. (11) Some variation in quality, and therefore in patient outcomes, is inevitable because not all teams will perform in the same way. It is only by setting up systems which facilitate comparisons that the full range of performance can be appraised.

Furthermore, lower-value clinical care is largely impossible to detect unless systems are in place. If thousands of clinicians are diagnosing and treating patients in isolation without a system in place, it is not possible to detect variations in care, and, in particular, above-average treatment rates that could indicate inappropriate care and the presence of waste. There may be a valid reason why one surgical service is doing three times as many operations as another, but it is unlikely to be due to variation in need. Unless it is possible to compare two services while taking into account differences in need, it is not possible to find out whether there is unwarranted variation in policy and practice.

Thus, the contribution of systems to improve quality and outcome leads to the identification of services in which value may not be at the maximum.

How systems can reduce harm

All medical care has the potential to cause harm as well as good. Systems help to reduce harm by:

- Improving the quality of care;
- Reducing errors.

Improving the quality of care

Even when medical care is of the highest quality, adverse effects or harm can occur because all medical care carries a risk of harm. When the level of quality is not the highest, not only is the probability of a good outcome reduced, but the probability of a poor outcome or harm is increased (Figure 3.4). Thus, interventions to reduce unwarranted variation in quality, and those to improve quality, will reduce the likelihood of harm occurring, and increase the likelihood of a positive outcome for patients.

To give a simple example, developing a system for patients being admitted to hospital for elective surgery to have their risk of venous thrombo-embolism (VTE) assessed ensures that, if their risk is high, preventive measures can be taken.

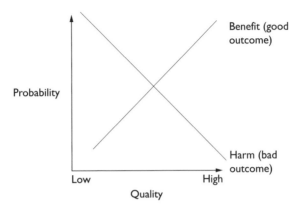

Figure 3.4 Relationship between quality of care and the likelihood of benefit and harm occurring

Reducing errors

Harm also results from errors.

> . . . *an error is the failure of planned actions to achieve their desired goal. There are basically two ways in which this failure can occur.*
>
> 1. *The plan is adequate, but the associated actions do not go as intended. These are failures of execution and are commonly termed slips and lapses. Slips relate to observable actions and are associated with attentional failures. Lapses are more internal events and relate to failures of memory.*
> 2. *The actions may go entirely as planned, but the plan is inadequate to achieve its intended outcome. These are failures of intention, termed mistakes. Mistakes can be further subdivided into rule based mistakes and knowledge based mistakes.* (12)

It has become clear that medical errors cannot be considered solely the responsibility of an individual, but can result from the lack of a system, and by relying too much on or blaming an individual. The need for a systems approach to error prevention is now widely accepted, and systems should be designed specifically to reduce the risk of errors occurring.

One aspect of healthcare for which a systems approach has already been adopted is patient safety. The impact of systems thinking on patient safety is outlined by Robert Wachter in his book, *Understanding Patient Safety*.

> *The modern patient safety movement replaces 'the blame and shame game' with a new approach, known as* systems thinking. *This paradigm acknowledges the human condition – namely, that humans err – and concludes that safety depends on creating systems that anticipate errors and either prevent or catch them before they cause harm. Such an approach has been the cornerstone of safety improvements in other high-risk industries but has been ignored in medicine until recently.* (13)

This quotation highlights the shift from individual responsibility as the only factor worth considering when a medical error occurs to one in which both systems and culture also need to be taken into account. In addition to the skill, competence and motivation of an individual, it is the environment in which an individual works that is a key factor, as Charles Vincent describes in his book, *Patient Safety*.

> *The essential idea underlying this approach is that errors and human behavior cannot be understood in isolation, but only in relation to the context in which people are working. Clinical staff are influenced by the nature of the task they are carrying out, the team they work in, their working environment and the wider organizational context; these are the system factors. From this perspective errors are seen not too much as the product of personal fallibility but as consequences of more general problems in the working environment.* (14)

Even if no errors are made, complicated processes can go wrong simply because, multiple events, none of which is critical, occur simultaneously by chance, resulting in what Charles Perrow calls a 'normal accident'

> *If interactive, complexity and tight coupling – system characteristics – inevitably will produce an accident, I believe we are justified in calling it a normal accident, or a system accident. The*

odd term normal accident is meant to signal that, given the system characteristics, multiple and unexpected interactions of failures are inevitable. This is an expression of an integral characteristic of the system, not a statement of frequency. (15)

How systems can reduce waste, and maximise value

Muda is the Japanese word for waste.

Waste or muda is any activity in a process that consumes resources without adding value for the customer. (16)

Waste can be defined as any activity that does not contribute to the desired outcome of a business. Waste is not confined to refuse. The most important book about the Japanese war on waste has the word 'system' in its title: *The Toyota Production System.* (16) The development of systems allows any low-value or wasteful components to be identified and removed thereby ensuring that all the resources used produce value. Value is a concept that is now accepted as being of greater importance than quality and outcome because it relates both of them to the use of resources. Michael Porter's definition of value makes this concept clear.

Value in any field must be defined around the customer, not the supplier. Value must also be measured by outputs, not inputs. Hence it is patient health results that matter, not the volume of services delivered. But results are achieved at some cost. Therefore, the proper objective is the value of health care delivery, or the patient health outcomes relative to the total cost (inputs) of attaining those outcomes. Efficiency, then, is subsumed in the concept of value. So are other objectives like safety, which is one aspect of outcomes. (17)

The beneficial effects of systems on quality and safety described thus far will also reduce waste.

However, systems offer additional benefits that increase value even when quality has been improved and harm reduced. A systems approach can ensure that:

- Value is increased by optimising allocative efficiency;

- The right patients receive the service being provided, that is, the patients who would derive most value from it;
- The right patients receive the right care;
- The right care provided to the right patients is provided at the lowest possible cost.

How systems increase value by optimising allocative efficiency

Alain Enthoven defined allocative efficiency as:

> *An efficient allocation of health care resources to and within the health care sector is one that minimizes the social cost of illness, including its treatment. This is achieved when the marginal dollar spent on health care produces the same value to society as the marginal dollar spent on education, defense, personal consumption, and other uses. Relevant costs include the suffering and inconvenience of patients, as well as the resources used in producing health care. This goal should not be confused with minimizing or containing health care services, often as a share of gross national product (GNP). But, a lower percentage of GNP spent on health car does not necessarily mean greater efficiency. If the reduced share of GNP is achieved by denial or postponement of services that consumers would value at more than their marginal cost, then efficiency is not achieved or enhanced by the cut in spending.* (18)

Value is maximised when the allocation of resources among different programmes of care is such that it is not possible to gain more benefit by switching a single pound from one budget to another. Traditionally, budgets have been set in a way that requires decision-makers to decide whether to switch money from primary care to secondary care, or vice versa, but it is much clearer to compare the budget for one system with that of another within the context of a programme budget. For example, within the programme budget for Problems of Vision, it is possible to compare the effects of increasing or decreasing the budgets for the systems for managing:

- Glaucoma;
- Cataract;

- Diabetic retinopathy;
- Macular degeneration.

The Problems of Vision budget itself has to compete for resources with other programme budgets, each of which also has a number of systems budgets within it, for example, the Problems of the Respiratory System programme budget has systems budgets for asthma, sleep apnoea, and bronchitis. These systems of care are the core businesses of healthcare, and not 'hospital' and 'community' services which usually form the bases for budgets.

How systems increase value by ensuring the service sees the right patients

Broken legs are simple: the right patients reach the right specialist service. However, for chronic conditions, this is not necessarily the case, as shown in Figure 3.5.

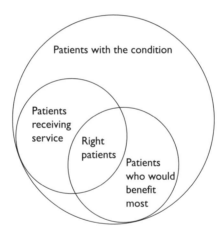

Figure 3.5 Relationship between need for and use of health services

Using systems it is possible to

- Minimise over-diagnosis;
- Encourage the referral of those patients who would benefit most;
- Develop the skills of generalists so that they can provide higher-

quality care to people who can be managed without direct contact with specialists.

Over-diagnosis is a 21st century epidemic caused by:

- The offer and uptake of screening tests despite the lack of evidence of benefit;
- The indiscriminate and uncritical use of imaging and laboratory tests;
- The promotion of spurious new disease entities by some pharmaceutical companies.

The referral of patients most likely to benefit from a specialist service can be increased by having explicit systems of care, including care pathways, which set out clearly the indications for referral. It is obvious that increasing the number of higher-value referrals creates pressure on a specialist service which has to be met, if additional resources for expansion are not available, by reducing the number of inappropriate referrals. The referral guidance in a pathway will contribute to reducing inappropriate referrals, but the specialist service also has to increase the capacity of the generalist service to provide good-quality care to people who are not referred. Both the encouragement of referrals of appropriate patients to the specialist service and the discouragement of referrals of inappropriate patients require a transformation of care during which health service structures – primary and secondary care, health centres and hospitals – become less important than the establishment of a system of care.

There is a need to move from a model of 'two-box healthcare' (Figure 3.6) to one of 'four-box healthcare' (Figure 3.7). In the two-box care model, the boxes represent 'the hospital' and 'the community', connected by patient referrals and discharges. The language is counterproductive because it implies that the hospital is not part of the community, nor is it a service for the community. Despite this, the two-box model has been the dominant paradigm for decades. In this paradigm, the hospital was a location at which acute crises were dealt with, e.g. broken legs, and perforated peptic ulcers. However, the principal healthcare challenge of the 21st century is people with long-term conditions, who need to receive four types of care. This is best

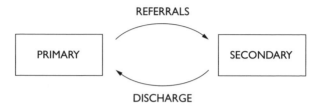

Figure 3.6 Two-box healthcare

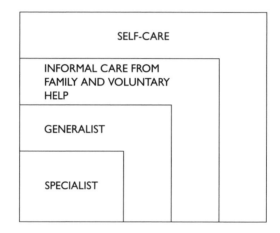

Figure 3.7 Four-box healthcare

represented by a Venn diagram, which shows that these four types of care – five, if a 'superspecialist' is involved – are nested within one another (19). Unfortunately, although the four-box model of healthcare is better in theory than in practice:

- Some people who need it get no professional help;
- Some people get only generalist care when they need specialist care;
- Some people get specialist care when they need only generalist care.

The radical nature of the transformation that a specialist service must undertake to meet the needs of the whole population, and not simply the needs of the patients referred to the specialist service, cannot be expressed in Figures 3.6 and 3.7. This transformation requires the specialist service:

- to provide support for generalists;
- to identify ways in which networks of care can be developed;
- to ensure that all patients have access to clear and unbiased information about their condition.

This new approach, already adopted by some specialist services, has been called 'population medicine', in which 21st century clinicians have a commitment to the population they serve that does not diminish their commitment to the individual patients who happen to have been referred to them. A companion volume, entitled *How To Practise Population Medicine*, will deal with these issues in greater depth.

How systems increase value by ensuring the right patients receive the right care

The most obvious waste of resource is a treatment for which there is no evidence of effectiveness. However, even where there is evidence of effectiveness, an intervention can be of low value if it is given to a patient whose profile is different from the profile of patients in the research study in which evidence of effectiveness was demonstrated. Although it is easy to blame clinicians for doing this, their decision-making is not helped by the fact that in too much research a new treatment is compared with placebo and not with the best current treatment. Comparative effectiveness research (CER) has been developed to halt this practice of comparing new treatments against placebo.

The IOM report states that CER is 'the generation and synthesis of evidence that compares the benefits and harms of alternative methods to prevent, diagnose, treat, and monitor a clinical condition or to improve the delivery of care'. The purpose of CER is to assist consumers, clinicians, purchasers, and policymakers to make informed decisions that will improve health care at both the individual and population levels. (20)

A system with an explicit pathway can set out clearly the right care for both clinicians and patients to see. However, care is not static. It evolves continuously with clinicians starting and stopping tests and treatments, often not in the context of a research study designed to test the comparative effectiveness of the innovation. If systems are in place, change can be managed explicitly and consistently. When a system is in place, the introduction of new technology of proven value is relatively straightforward: key staff can be identified, training can be organised, and equipment purchased and phased in. With a system in place, if a service wishes to introduce change, it is possible to identify which aspect of the existing system should be discontinued or modified. This allows for budgetary control and the prevention of technology creep. The establishment of the National Institute of Health and Clinical Excellence (NICE) in England allowed the NHS to tackle the problems of budgetary overspend and technology creep by establishing a system for managing the appraisal of new technology and knowledge.

Furthermore, systems in which what is thought to be the right care is defined allow clinicians to identify variations in practice that could indicate important uncertainties. When an area of uncertainty has been identified, it can be classified as:

- uncertain uncertainty – we do not know if there is a reliable answer;
- certain uncertainty – we do know there is not a reliable answer.

The Database of Uncertainties about the Effectiveness of Treatments (DUETs), www.duets.nhs.uk, is a system in which 'certain uncertainties' are identified, and collected in a database. Information in the database is then distributed to research funders to support the prioritisation of research topics, and to patients and clinicians to be considered during clinical decision-making.

How systems increase value by ensuring the right patients receive the right care with the lowest possible use of resources

The use of resources that are unnecessary denies those resources to other patients, and the need for lean healthcare is now widely accepted. Toussaint and Gerard have adapted the seven types of wastes identified by Taiichi Ohno in Toyota, and developed the 'Eight Wastes of Lean Healthcare' (21):

1. Defect: making errors, correcting errors, inspecting work already done for error

2. Waiting: for test results to be delivered, for an appointment, for a bed
3. Motion: searching for supplies, fetching drugs from another room, looking for proper forms
4. Transportation: taking patients through miles of corridors, from one test to the next unnecessarily, transferring patients to new rooms or units, carrying trays of tools between rooms
5. Overproduction: excessive diagnostic testing, unnecessary treatment
6. Overprocessing: a patient being asked the same question three times, unnecessary forms, nurses writing everything in a chart instead of noting exceptions
7. Inventory: (too much or too little); overstocked drugs expiring on the shelf, understocked surgical supplies delaying procedures while staff go in search of needed items
8. Talent: failing to listen to employees' ideas for improvement.

The health services that have successfully reduced waste have used both culture change and systems of care to do so.

Measures to save money almost always save carbon. It is vital that health services reduce their carbon footprint and increase the sustainability of healthcare, not simply because they will be required to do so, but also because it is their ethical duty to contribute to reducing the principal threat to health in the 21st century, that of climate change. The Centre for Sustainable Healthcare (formerly the Campaign for Greener Healthcare) and the NHS Sustainable Development Unit (SDU) are committed to this end. Carbon will become the new currency for health services.

The electricity bill for the NHS is probably about £400 million per annum. It would be relatively easy to release about £20 million by increasing energy efficiency and thereby help to fund higher-value healthcare, while reducing the NHS's environmental impact. However, heating and lighting are not the principal generators of carbon emissions during the provision of healthcare. Travel by staff, patients and visitors, and the manufacture of drugs and medical devices, are much more significant sources of carbon emissions. The majority of carbon is generated as a direct result of clinical practice and not by the built healthcare estate.

The 21st century requires a style of clinical practice in which:

- Every clinician is involved in prevention;
- The patient is at the centre of care doing as much for themselves as possible;
- Pathways of care, expressions of the systems, have all unnecessary steps stripped out;
- The treatments for a service are chosen taking into account the carbon footprint as well as the financial cost.

For a sustainable health service, we need not only sustainable infrastructure, but also sustainable clinical practice. We need sustainable systems of care, systems that we can envisage being delivered in 20 years' time.

How systems can reduce health inequalities and inequities

It is important to distinguish between two similar-sounding, but quite different, concepts: 'equality' and 'equity'. The former implies equal shares of something; the latter, a 'fair' or 'just' distribution, which may or may not result in equal shares. (22)

It is only by the development of population-based systems of care that inequalities in the amount of service delivered can be measured. Health inequalities, increased rates of disease in certain subgroups of the population, have long been recognised, but health service inequalities have been recognised only recently due principally to the pioneering work of Jack Wennberg, who produced *The Dartmouth Atlas of Health Care* (23), which inspired the *NHS Atlas of Variation in Healthcare* (24). Inequalities in the provision of health services are sometimes warranted, for example, it is essential to have more services for people with sickle cell disease in urban than in rural areas. However, much variation is unwarranted, that is, not justified by differences in need but results from the lack of systems of care that relate resources to need. As such, the variation represents an inequity in health service provision. Thus, it is of greater concern when there is not only inequality but inequity in the provision of healthcare in relation to need.

The relationship of variation in activity to variation in need can

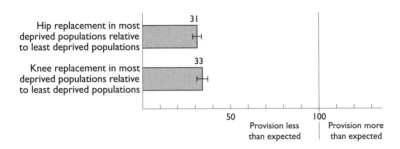

Figure 3.8 Inequities in the provision of hip and knee replacement (25)

highlight inequity as a study of joint replacement in England showed (see Figure 3.8). Judge et al. found that the most deprived populations had the lowest rate of hip and knee replacement (25), and concluded that '*people in affluent areas got most care relative to need*', an example of Julian Tudor Hart's Inverse Care Law. (26)

Systems can be given a specific focus on both inequality and inequity. For instance, by setting an objective such as 'To reduce inequality of access to resources for subgroups in the population who have the greatest need but in whom service use is lowest' will reduce the impact of the Inverse Care Law.

How systems can improve the prevention of disease

The type of health service that is of the highest value is the prevention of disease and disability. The prevention of disease also requires a systems approach and, because of the underlying philosophy of public health, disease prevention is already more systems-orientated than much of clinical care. Screening and vaccination services are good examples of systems of prevention, and the same approach should be adopted for the range of preventable diseases, such as those related to smoking, although there are more complex issues involved which require the application of a soft systems methodology (see Chapter 2).

It can also be useful to include within every clinical care system an objective related to prevention. This will prompt clinicians to seek to have an influence on the causes or determinants of the diseases they treat, such as cigarette smoking in the case of heart disease or alcohol-

65

related violence in the case of trauma care, through the exercise, if only for a small amount of their limited time, of their charismatic authority.

The potential of health services to prevent disease is limited partly due to the fact that the major causes of disease are socio-economic, but there are some diseases that every health service can prevent, such as hospital-acquired venous thrombo-embolism (VTE) and familial hypercholesterolaemia (FH). These diseases require focused systems, which are lacking in most health services.

Disease prevention is the best-value health service.

Questions for reflection or for use in network building or teaching

If using these questions during network building or teaching, ask the group to work in pairs, and reflect on one of the questions for three minutes; try to get people who do not know one another to work together.

When taking feedback, let each pair make only one point. In the interests of equity, if you start with the pair on the left-hand side of the room for the first question, start with the pair on the right-hand side of the room for the second question.

- Why is it becoming more difficult to manage healthcare?
- If more money was available but could not be used simply to expand healthcare as it is today, what would be your priority for investment?
- If no more money was available, what would be your priorities for disinvestment?
- What arguments would you use to persuade a management team who had never discussed systems of care that a systems approach would offer low-cost solutions to their principal problems?

References

(1) Castells, M. (2009) *The Information Age: Economy, Society and Culture. Volume 1: The Rise Of The Network Society*. Second edition. Wiley-Blackwell.

(2) Timmermans, S. and Berg, M. (2003) *The Gold Standard. The Challenge of Evidence-Based Medicine and Standardization in Health Care*. Temple University Press, Philadelphia.

(3) Whittaker, D. (editor) (2009) *Think before you Think: Social Complexity and Knowledge of Knowing*. [Anthology of Stafford Beer's papers, reviews, talks, poetry and art.] Wavestone Press.

(4) Sweeney, K. (2006) *Complexity in Primary Care: understanding its value*. Radcliffe Publishing Ltd.

(5) Ishikawa, K. (1985) *What is Total Quality Control? The Japanese Way*. Prentice Hall.

(6) Morgan, J. M. and Liker, J. K. (2006) *The Toyota Product Development System. Integrating People, Process, and Technology*. Productivity Press, New York.

(7) Black, J. R. with Miller, D. (2008) *The Toyota Way to Healthcare Excellence. Increase Efficiency and Improve Quality with Lean*. Health Administration Press.

(8) Peters, T. J. and Waterman, R. H. (1984) *In Search of Excellence*. HarperCollins.

(9) Collins, J. C. and Porras, J. I. (1994) *Built to Last. Successful Habits of Visionary Companies*. HarperBusiness.

(10) Collins, J. C. (2001) *Good to Great. Why some companies make the leap . . . and others don't*. Random House Business.

(11) Grove, A. S. (1995) *High Output Management*. Vintage Books.

(12) Vincent, C. (editor) (2001) *Clinical Risk Management. Enhancing patient safety*. Second edition. BMJ Books.

(13) Wachter, R. M. (2007) *Understanding Patient Safety*. McGraw-Hill Medical.

(14) Vincent, C. (2010) *Patient Safety*. Second edition. Wiley-Blackwell and BMJ Books.

(15) Perrow, C. (1999) *Normal Accidents. Living with High-Risk Technologies*. Princeton University Press.

(16) Ohno, T. (1988) *Toyota Production System. Beyond Large-Scale Production*. Productivity Press.

(17) Porter, M. E. and Teisberg, E. O. (2006) *Redefining Health Care: Creating Value-Based Competition on Results*. Harvard Business School Press.

(18) Enthoven, A. C. and Smith, K. W. (2005) *How Much is Enough? Shaping the Defense Program 1961–1969*. RAND Corporation.

(19) Gray, J. A. M. (1983) Four Box Healthcare: Development in a Time of

Zero Growth. *Lancet* 322: 1185–1186. doi: 10.1016/S0140–6736(83)91227–8

(20) Sox, H. C. (2010) Comparative Effectiveness Research: A Progress Report. *Ann Intern Med* 153: 469–472. Available at: http://annals. org/content/153/7/469.full

(21) Toussaint, J. and Gerrard, R. A. (2010) *On the Mend. Revolutionizing Healthcare to Save Lives and Transform the Industry.* Lean Enterprise Institute.

(22) Rice, T. H. (1998) *The Economics of Health Reconsidered.* Health Administration Press.

(23) Wennberg, J. E. (1998) *The Dartmouth Atlas of Health Care.* American Hospital Association.

(24) Right Care (2010) *The NHS Atlas of Variation in Healthcare: Reducing unwarranted variation to increase value and improve quality.* November 2010. QIPP. Available at: http://www.rightcare.nhs.uk

(25) Judge, A., Welton, N. J., Sandhu, J. and Ben-Shlomo, Y. (2010) Equity in access to total joint replacement of the hip and knee in England. *Br Med J* 2010;341:c4092 doi: 10.1136/bmj.c4092 (Published 11 August 2010)

(26) Tudor Hart, J. (1971) Inverse Care Law. *Lancet* i; 405–412.

4

HOW DO SYSTEMS PLAY THEIR PART IN 21ST CENTURY HEALTHCARE?

This chapter will:
- describe the relationship between bureaucracies and systems;
- describe the relationship between systems and culture;
- analyse the criticisms that systems reduce clinical freedom and make care less personal.

By the end of the chapter you will have developed an understanding of:
- the benefits and limitations of bureaucracies;
- how the claim that using systems makes care less humane can be refuted;
- how the argument that the introduction of systems does serious harm to professional freedom can be countered.

Touchstone: Bureaucracy as Janus

Kafka's description of Gregor Samsa's metamorphosis into a beetle is one of the enduring images of 20th century literature, but Kafka is perhaps more widely known for the eponymous adjective 'Kafka-esque', which encapsulates the feelings of bafflement, apprehension and fear an individual experiences when they seek to engage with, or are ensnared by, a bureaucracy.

Kafka's novel *The Castle* captures, to a greater extent than *The Trial*, the malign face of bureaucracy but, like the Roman god Janus, bureaucracy has two faces, one of which is benign. Those who have worked in organisations in which the word of a capricious chief is law, not uncommon in the clinical world, will appreciate the merits of bureaucracies described in this chapter.

However, bureaucracies, which have been the preoccupation of health policy-makers and re-organisers for the last 50 years, are less important than systems or culture.

The context for systems within a health service can be expressed using the simple model shown in Figure 4.1.

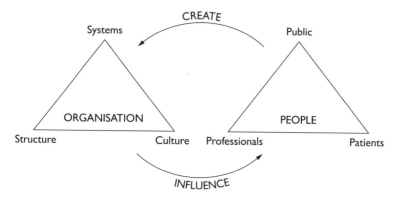

Figure 4.1 Context for systems within a health service

In addition to the elements shown in Figure 4.1, all parts of a health service are influenced by incentives, rewards, and regulations. Although the focus of this book is systems, systems do not act in isolation; they are influenced by people, culture, and the structure of the organisation.

Systems and structure

Types of authority

Max Weber (1) described three different types of authority:

1. bureaucratic authority;
2. charismatic authority;
3. sapiential authority, that is, authority derived from knowledge.

Much of his work focused on bureaucratic authority, which, in the early part of the 20th century, was replacing charismatic authority in both government and business.

In healthcare, the charismatic authority of the doctor dominated decision-making for the first half of the 20th century. In the second half of the 20th century, as healthcare became more complex – partly as the result of the introduction of new technologies such as radiotherapy and transplantation – and financial investment increased, bureaucratic authority increased. Some people believe that the charismatic authority of the medical profession has declined significantly in the last decade as 'consumers', the patients, have become more critical, and as medical errors have become more apparent.

Inter-relationship between systems and bureaucracies

A system can be regarded as a type of organisation that is based on knowledge or sapiential authority; such a system is able to co-exist with one or more bureaucracies.

Much of the work to appraise the inter-relationship between bureaucracies and systems has been done in Japan. In *The Knowledge-Creating Company*, Ikujiro Nonaka and Hirotaka Takeuchi investigated how Japanese companies were not only good at production-line engineering but also at creating new products and services. They found companies did this by creating networks within a bureaucracy, and concluded that:

> *a business organization should have a non-hierarchical, self-organizing structure working in tandem with its hierarchal formal structure. As business organization is growing in scale and complexity, they should simultaneously maximise both corporate level efficiency and local flexibility. The most appropriate name is the hypertext organization.* (2)

The term 'hypertext organisation' was introduced in 1995, at an early point in the development of the Internet. The hypertext organisation, like the World Wide Web, can be configured in any way, and formed into the most appropriate configuration for the particular task in hand, whereas bureaucracies are hierarchical organisations with information flows from either top to bottom, or bottom to top.

The relationship between a bureaucracy and a hypertext organisation is depicted in Figure 4.2.

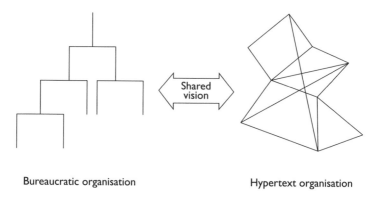

Bureaucratic organisation   Hypertext organisation

Figure 4.2 Bureaucratic and hypertext organisations

The intelligent bureaucracy is one that not only keeps control of those aspects of business that have to be managed carefully, for example, the employment of staff or the oversight of money, but also encourages the development of hypertext organisations or systems for service delivery, and innovation.

Subsequent empirical work by Mitsuru Kodama, described in *Project-Based Organization in the Knowledge-Based Society* (3), shows how effective Japanese industries are at working not only within a single bureaucracy but also across bureaucracies. This approach is described in several books on the Toyota Way (4, 5). Toyota is a phenomenal company, which has had a marked influence on other companies, and on the global healthcare sector, until its reputation was dented by the recall of millions of cars worldwide due to concern about an engineering fault. The subsequent independent investigation showed that there was no fault with the cars' engineering, the electrics or the production system, but, in retrospect, the company's handling of the problem through public relations was clumsy (6).

Thus, systems and bureaucracies need not be in competition, and should be seen as complementary.

Tensions between systems and bureaucracies

However, there are tensions when setting up and running a system across several bureaucracies. Although different parts of the system have different responsibilities, there is the potential for one or more of the bureaucracies in the system to duplicate resources or even to compete.

Concept applied to healthcare: In a Stroke Management and Prevention Service, although there is a need for neuro-imaging facilities, it is possible that two hospitals in the same system both want to establish imaging services as part of their development as major teaching centres (bureaucracies often serve their own interests). In such a situation, those with financial authority who are responsible for investing resources need to ensure that the system is designed as efficiently as possible without unnecessary duplication of expensive resources.

In summary, therefore, bureaucracies and systems can have tensions between them, but the intelligent bureaucracy makes use of systems not only within the bureaucracy but also in its relationships with other bureaucracies. Hospitals and primary care need to work together as part of one system and, as healthcare becomes increasingly complex, hospitals also need to work together as part of one system.

In praise of bureaucracy

Bureaucracies can be a force for good. In bureaucracies, decisions are made by the rulebook, and the effect can be to limit the power of capricious or venal officials, in theory at least, to an interpretation of the rules and their application in an individual case. Charles Perrow, one of the most highly regarded sociologists studying organisations, outlined the benefits of bureaucracies.

'Bureaucracy' is a dirty word, both to the average person and to many specialists on organizations. It suggests rigid rules and regulations, a hierarchy of offices, narrow specialization of personnel, an abundance of offices or units which can hamstring those who want to get things done, impersonality, resistance to change. Yet every organization of any significant size is bureaucratized to some degree or, to put it differently, exhibits more or

less stable patterns of behaviour based upon a structure of roles and specialized tasks. Bureaucracy, in this sense, is another word for structure.

Most of the key elements of the rational-legal bureaucracy are represented in this brief case history. They include:

1. *Equal treatment for all employees.*
2. *Reliance on expertise, skills, and experience relevant to the position.*
3. *No extraorganizational prerogatives of the position (such as taking dynamite, wallboard, etc.); that is, the position is seen as belonging to the organization, not the person. The employee cannot use it for personal ends.*
4. *Specific standards of work and output.*
5. *Extensive record keeping dealing with the work and output.*
6. *Establishment and enforcement of rules and regulations that serve the interests of the organization.*
7. *Recognition that rules and regulations bind managers as well as employees; thus employees can hold management to the terms of the employment contract.* (7)

A health service needs a good bureaucracy, and a system cannot function without good bureaucratic support. An exemplary system in the NHS is the National Fetal Assessment Programme, which evolved from the National Down's Syndrome Screening Programme. This system depended upon:

- 152 primary care trusts with budgets;
- 150 hospitals employing clinicians.

The National Fetal Assessment Programme, as a system, enabled 302 bureaucracies to work in a coordinated way, and could not have functioned without them.

Systems and culture

Edgar Schein, one of the gurus of culture in management, defined culture as:

a pattern of shared basic assumptions that was learned by a group as it solved its problems of external adaptation and internal integration, that has worked well enough to be con-sidered valid and, therefore, to be taught to new members as the correct way to perceive, think, and feel in relation to those problems. (8)

A health service, such as a hospital, can have several co-existing cultures: for instance, an official culture, a sub-culture in the theatre suite, and a bullying culture, to name but three. The official culture is expressed by an organisation's mission statement, and usually, but not always, reflected in the behaviour of hospital personnel, particularly those who have managerial and leadership responsibilities.

A hospital has many similarities with other types of organisation, such as software companies, universities or insurance companies, and the culture of a hospital shares many characteristics with the cultures of other large organisations. Some organisational cultures are inno-vative, others are risk averse; some encourage employees to criticise and speak out, others value more deferential behaviour. However, a health service needs to have a culture that has certain distinctive characteristics which differentiate it from the culture of a car factory or an insurance company.

Many health services now have a culture that:

- puts the patient at the centre of care, not the clinician;
- values patient safety above all other aspects of quality;
- perceives themselves as knowledge businesses as well as caring businesses.

For a health service, such as a hospital, to contribute effectively when working as part of a system, as well as when working as an independent organisation, it must have a culture of respect, not only for patients but also for the clinicians who work at other hospitals. If a hospital wishes to be a good partner within a system of care for people with rheumatoid arthritis, the Professor of Rheumatology must accept that he is no more important than a newly qualified pharmacist dispensing medication in a small town 50 miles away or a general practitioner with a special interest in the management of the condi-tion. Similarly, the Chief Executive of that hospital has to resist the culture of growth and control and, through leadership, create a culture of partnership and collaboration.

Systems need to support people

We developed a form of warfare based on . . . the high quality of the individual soldier, his morale, toughness and discipline, his acceptance of hardship and his ability to move on his own feet and to look after himself.

Viscount Slim, *Defeat Into Victory* (1956)

Although clinical practice is organised through systems, it is delivered by individual clinicians, communicating with patients during consultations, and making decisions with, or without, patient involvement. The consultation lies at the heart of the healthcare process. In England, there are about 2,000,000 consultations, and 10,000,000 clinical decisions made every day. These consultations and decisions determine:

- patient outcome;
- patient experience;
- resource use.

For too long it was believed that by organising the bureaucracy correctly, the problems of controlling healthcare spending, improving the quality of healthcare and improving patient safety could be managed. It is necessary, however, to recognise that many clinical decisions take place outside the consultation (see Figure 4.3).

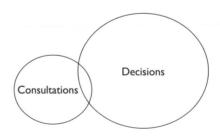

Figure 4.3 Consultations and decisions

Furthermore, although patients are active partners in decision-making, only a proportion of decisions are shared (see Figure 4.4).

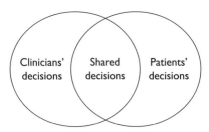

Figure 4.4 Shared decisions

Interventions to improve the performance of individuals vary widely, but can be classified into three types:

- educational interventions, designed to improve knowledge and skill;
- motivational interventions, designed to improve performance;
- regulatory interventions, designed to prevent poor performance.

In the first half of the 20th century, a doctor worked in relative isolation, with very few effective treatments, but often with high levels of trust from patients, which are now diminishing in both the United Kingdom and the United States of America (9). In the second half of the 20th century, the development of effective, expensive treatments led to increased investment in bigger institutions, with a consequent increase in bureaucracy. The growing influence of financial systems, legal systems and bio-ethics is an inevitable consequence of the bureaucratisation of healthcare.

The forces that increase the need for systems can also increase the number of people involved in management. 'Consumerism' has led citizens to demand more open, accountable services and higher-quality products, which in turn has made clinicians more open and clinical practice more explicit. Rothman describes this transformation in the introduction to his book *Strangers at the Bedside*, which deals with 'Making the Invisible Visible'.

By the mid-1970s, both the style and the substance of medical decision making had changed. The authority that an individual physician had once exercised overtly was now subject to debate and review by colleagues and laypeople. Let the physician design a research protocol to deliver an experimental treatment, and in the room, by general mandate, was an institutional review board composed of other physicians, lawyers, and community representatives to make certain that the potential benefits to the subject-patient outweighed the risks. Let the physician attempt to allocate a scarce resource, like a donor heart, and in the room were federal and state legislators and administrators to help set standards of equity and justice. Let the physician decide to withdraw or terminate life-sustaining treatment from an incompetent patient, and in the room were state judges to rule, in advance, on the legality of these actions. Such a decision might also bring into the room a hospital ethics committee staffed by an unusual cadre of commentators, the bioethicists, who stood ready to replace bedside ethics with armchair ethics, to draw on philosophers' first principles, not on the accumulated experience of medical practice. (10)

In this book, we are interested in healthcare systems that focus on *clinical* problems, but the pressure from other systems – finance, law, ethics – on both clinicians and those who pay for or manage healthcare is difficult to over-emphasise, particularly to people who have never had to make a difficult clinical decision.

Healthcare is a hybrid organisation, as defined by Andy Grove of Intel, who described the way in which functional units and mission-orientated units work together, and the accompanying principle of dual reporting. However, Grove pointed out that hybrid organisations, like democracies:

are not great in and of themselves. They just happen to be the best way for any business to be organised (11).

Systems and personalised medicine

The key question for the organisation in the 21st century is to ask, 'What is the role of the human being?'
Bill Gates (12)

Variability is the law of life, and as no two faces are the same, so no two bodies are alike, and no two individuals react alike and behave alike under the abnormal conditions which we know as disease.

William Osler

Although the assertion that 'every patient is different' has its limitations when used as an argument against the implementation of guidelines, it is true in the context of the clinical consultation. Every patient *is* different, and the role of the doctor, as human being, is to relate the evidence derived from studies of groups of patients to the unique clinical condition and values of the patient sitting in front of them.

Evidence-based medicine, the application of clinical epidemiology at the bedside, has introduced techniques to reduce clinicians' reliance on heuristics. The practice of evidence-based medicine has been defined as:

> *... the conscientious, explicit, and judicious use of current best evidence in making decisions about the care of individual patients. The practice of evidence based medicine means integrating individual clinical expertise with the best available external clinical evidence from systematic research. By individual clinical expertise we mean the proficiency and judgement that individual clinicians acquire through clinical experience and clinical practice.* (13)

With the advent of evidence-based medicine, relating the evidence base to the particular risk profile of an individual has become more explicit and more scientific (Figure 4.5). There is also a better understanding of how to measure and manage patients' preferences, both for different outcomes and for different styles of decision-making. As patient preference varies, it is always important to ascertain a patient's values and expectations prior to taking any decisions.

Thus, the input of a human being is still necessary. This approach has been called 'personalised medicine' by Peter Rothwell:

> *... the two key questions that are most frequently asked by clinicians about applying the results of randomised controlled trials and systematic reviews to decisions about their individual*

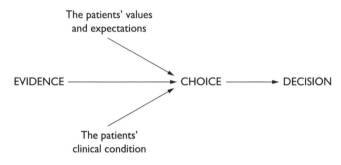

Figure 4.5 The decision-making process

patients. Is the evidence relevant to my clinical practice? How can I judge whether the probability of benefit from treatment in my current patient is likely to differ substantially from the average probability of benefit reported in the relevant trial or systematic review? (14)

Developments in genetics will enable greater personalisation or, in the words of Christensen et al., greater precision.

We define precision medicine as the provision of care for diseases that can be precisely diagnosed, whose causes are understood, and which consequently can be treated with rules-based therapies that are predictably effective.
Another term 'personalized medicine' is often used for this phenomenon that we're calling 'precision medicine.' (15)

Decision support systems can help with the process of personalisation, but they have limitations, and when under pressure to make decisions the clinician often has to employ 'bounded rationality' (16), using 'fast and frugal heuristics' (17), as described in real-world settings by writers such as Atul Gawande (18) and Jerome Groopman (19). How else can clinicians complete the morning clinic in the time allotted? Without the use of bounded rationality by individual clinicians, even the best-designed system would collapse.

Relating the research evidence to a particular patient's risk profile is not easy:

- evidence may not exist;
- the existing evidence may not be strong;
- if strong evidence does exist, it may not be directly relevant to the particular patient a clinician is treating; the research may have been done on patients with a different profile from the presenting patient who might be older or have other diseases or risk factors.

Evidence is derived from groups of patients and, often, the group is a defined subset of the whole population. For instance, the patients in a heart failure trial may be under the age of 70 years, and have no other complicating diagnoses. The entry criteria for patients accepted for the trial will have been specified in this way to reduce the number of 'confounding' factors when the data are analysed. Clinical practice is, however, full of confounding factors. For example, the patient presenting could be 82 years old and, in addition to having a clinical problem for which there is no strong evidence of effective treatment, has three other diseases and is already taking five other drugs.

Once the evidence has been related to the unique clinical condition of the individual, the clinician then has to help the patient reflect on the options they have, how the options relate to their values, and the choice they face. Computerised decision support systems have a part to play in this process. For instance, there are software programmes that allow a pregnant woman to be given an accurate assessment of the risk that her fetus has Trisomy 21 (Down's syndrome). This probability is computed by taking into account the pregnant woman's age, the duration of the pregnancy, and the results of biochemical and ultrasound tests. There are also computerised decision support programmes that help patients to reflect on the choice they face, for example, by listening to the stories of other people who have faced the same dilemma; the Foundation for Informed Medical Decision Making has a range of such decision aids.

Systems and clinical freedom

In the past, 'clinical freedom' often meant that each clinician did whatever they wanted. However, Isaiah Berlin defined two concepts of liberty – positive and negative (20). Negative liberty is the amount of freedom an individual has to do what they want. In a clinical context, an example of negative liberty would be the freedom to prescribe any drug. Positive liberty is the amount of freedom an individual has to determine how much negative liberty they have. For a clinician, an example of positive liberty would be the degree of influence they have on the development of prescribing guidelines, usually exercised through the relevant professional organisation.

Although systems limit negative liberty, they need not reduce clinical freedom. Indeed, the participation of the medical profession in the development of guidelines, and the systems designed to implement those guidelines, can help to maintain the profession's clinical freedom by exercising positive liberty to limit the negative liberty of its members. The medical profession needs to be aware of the distinction between the two types of liberty, and the changing nature of the relationship between clinician and patient.

David Rothman, a Professor at Columbia University, has been critical of the American medical profession's opposition to policies that would have improved the health and healthcare of millions of low-income Americans (21). However, he is sympathetic to the plight of the individual clinician who has to take extremely difficult decisions, not only under the pressure of time but also under the pressure of working in systems developed by 'strangers', who are outsiders, and non-doctors (10).

Systems and the patient as an individual

The potential to tailor care during treatment

'You are just a number' is a common complaint made by patients about health services. When faced with being cared for by a 'system', some patients might be fearful of increasing regimentation and a decrease in the quality of experience, based on an assumption that all aspects of care would be standardised. However, standardisation is not an inevitable consequence of the introduction of systems. Systems should reduce the variability of certain technical aspects of care such as:

- the evidence on which clinicians base their decisions;
- the degree to which care deviates from the pathway recommended by a relevant guideline without good reason.

Evidence shows not only that patients differ in their preferred style of decision-making (22), but also that some clinicians are unable to discern a patient's preferred style and tend to offer all patients one style irrespective of an individual patient's wishes for self-determination, shared decision-making, or a paternalistic doctor (23). By building decision nodes into a care pathway, and designing appropriate decision aids (paper and computer-based), the patient's preferred style can be ascertained and accommodated at the relevant stages along the pathway.

The humanity of care

Few services have made the dramatic improvement in the quality of care and outcomes that the childhood leukaemia service has achieved during the last 20 years. What was once a fatal disease is now, in most cases, curable. The children receive care from a group of committed clinicians according to guidelines based on a systematic review of evidence from individual randomised controlled trials. Each child has the opportunity to be entered into one or more ongoing randomised controlled trials designed to increase the strength of the evidence base, to enhance the system, and to improve the child's treatment and/or outcome.

Although the treatment of childhood leukaemia is an example of protocols in action in a tightly controlled system, no service does better at individualising care, not only for the children affected but also for their parents, devastated by a diagnosis that still carries the connotation of a death sentence, and the treatment for which, though effective, can be distressing for all concerned.

Thus, the use of systems can increase the humanity of care, not decrease it, and the management of childhood leukaemia highlights the role a doctor can play as a human being working within a well-run system.

In contrast, clinicians who are trying to find lost notes to ascertain what has happened to the patient previously, or what should happen in future, are distracted and unable to do what human beings can do better than computers, that is, relate to, and empathise with, other human beings in distress.

The system as a state of calm

Patients' interactions with health services are usually confined to their experiences of consultations: the face-to-face interaction with a clinician, preceded and followed by encounters with administrative staff. Most patients do not want to think about systems any more than the proud purchaser of a new car wants to think about the car's production system. When care is provided as part of a system, the patient will experience not only consideration and competence at each consultation, but also the feeling of following a pathway (i.e. a route) through the system, rather like being on a guided tour to a foreign country, where there is the possibility that bad things can happen but not when you are being looked after by a competent tour operator.

The patient as constant

In the context of a fragmented workforce, only the patient is constant. If a patient is unconscious or severely ill, it is increasingly common for someone (usually a spouse or family member) to be with them to provide continuity.

We need to use the fact of the patient's constancy in several ways:

- by considering patients as key members of clinical teams;
- by building systems around patients.

Patient-held records not only enable patients to act as members of clinical teams, but also facilitate the building of systems around patients. Moreover, the innovation of patient-held records is an appropriate step for health services to take both morally and practically.

The resourceful patient

Evidence from studies of patients and clinicians demonstrates that:

- many patients want more information than they are getting at present; for some patient groups, the majority feel this way;
- many patients want more responsibility and involvement in decision-making than they are receiving at present;
- different patients have different preferred decision-making styles;

- a patient's preferred decision-making style cannot be predicted with complete confidence: to a certain extent, the higher the level of education, the greater a patient's desire for information, but there are some well-educated patients who want the doctor to take the decision, and some patients with low levels of education who want to be fully involved in the decision taken;
- clinicians are not good at identifying the preferred decision-making style of patients: in general, clinicians underestimate the patient's wish for information and involvement;
- the patient's desire for information is greater than the time allotted to a clinician in which to provide it (24).

When discussing these findings with clinicians, it is common for at least one person to say they know patients who do not desire more information and want the doctor to make the decision. Although this is true, it is important to emphasise that the argument is not that all patients must be involved in decision-making, simply that our starting assumption as healthcare providers should be that patients are competent and have a desire to be involved, with the ability to hand back responsibility to the clinician to the degree they choose. At present, the starting assumptions in most health services are that:

- patients are less intelligent, and therefore less able to understand and interpret clinical information;
- their information need is simply for a leaflet.

In the 21st century, we need to recognise that patients can be 'resourceful' if they are given access to the necessary resources. Other terms that could be used to describe a 'resourceful' patient are an 'autonomous' or 'expert' patient. However, the antonym or opposite of 'expert' is 'inexpert', which is depreciatory, whereas the adjective 'resourceful' has a paronym that is precise and not depreciatory – 'resource-less', i.e. lacking or deficient in resources. Those who pay for and manage health services must ensure that patients are provided with the resources they need to take part in decision-making and the management of their care. There is evidence, using conventional measures of performance and not simply patient satisfaction, that the management of care is better when patients are responsible for it. For example, a systems approach with the patient at its centre for the management of anticoagulation was able to achieve better outcomes than conventional care (25).

One type of information that patients should be offered once the decision has been made to treat them is information about the process of care they are due to follow, that is, the care pathway. Care pathways play an important part in the management of systems. A pathway not only describes a patient's progress through a system as they are cared for by a network of individuals and organisations, it also expresses and reinforces the system.

Some of the complaints revealed by surveys of patient experience relate to the chaos in which clinical care seems to be delivered. By focusing on the patient and the problems they have with the health service, as opposed to the problems they have with their disease, deficiencies in the system can be identified. Furthermore, by giving patients the opportunity of providing feedback on the performance of clinicians, using a tool like that developed by iWantGreatCare (www.iwantgreatcare.org), the system becomes cybernetic (see Chapter 1), with feedback being a feature common to all systems.

Systems eat structure for breakfast.

Questions for reflection when teaching or developing networks

If using these in network building or teaching, give one of the questions to the group and ask them to work in pairs to reflect on the question for three minutes; try to get people who do not know one another to work together.

When taking feedback, let each pair make only one point. In the interests of equity, if you start with the pair on the left-hand side of the room for the first question, start with the pair on the right-hand side of the room for the second question.

- Why might the chief executives of institutions like hospitals be reluctant to participate in systems development, and how could you overcome their reluctance?
- What is one of the best features about the culture in which you work, and what is one of the worst?
- If a group of clinicians were unenthusiastic about or hostile towards the proposal to develop a system of care, what steps would you take to change their beliefs and attitudes?

References

(1) Stanislav, A. (editor) (1983) *Max Weber on Capitalism, Bureaucracy and Religion.* Allen & Unwin.
(2) Nonaka, I. and Takeuchi, H. (1995) *The Knowledge-Creating Company: How Japanese Companies Create the Dynamics of Innovation.* Seventh edition. Oxford University Press, USA.
(3) Kodama, M. (2007) *Project-Based Organization in the Knowledge-Based Society: Innovation by Strategic Communities.* Imperial College Press.
(4) Liker, J. K. (2004) *The Toyota Way. 14 Management Principles from the World's Greatest Manufacturer.* McGraw-Hill.
(5) Osona, E., Shimizu, N. and Takeuchi, H. with Dorton, J. K. (2008) *Extreme Toyota. Radical Contradictions That Drive Success at the World's Best Manufacturer.* John Wiley & Sons.
(6) Liker, J. K. and Ogden, T. N. (2011) *Toyota Under Fire. Lessons for turning crisis into opportunity. How Toyota Faced the Challenges of Recall and the Recession to Come Out Stronger.* McGraw-Hill Professional.

(7) Perrow, C. (1986) *Complex Organizations: A Critical Essay.* Third edition. McGraw-Hill Higher Education.

(8) Schein, E. H. (2004) *Organizational Culture and Leadership.* Third edition. Jossey-Bass.

(9) O'Neill, O. (2002) *A Question of Trust. The BBC Reith Lectures 2002.* Cambridge University Press.

(10) Rothman, D. J. (2003) *Strangers at the Bedside. A History of How Law and Bioethics Transformed Medical Decision Making.* Aldine Transaction.

(11) Grove, A. S. (1995) *High Output Management.* Vintage Books.

(12) Gates, W. with Myhrvold, N. and Rinearson, P. (1995) *The Road Ahead.* Viking Penguin.

(13) Straus, S. E., Richardson, W. D., Glasziou, P. et al. (2005) *Evidence Based Medicine: How to Practice and Teach EBM.* Third edition. Churchill Livingstone, Edinburgh.

(14) Rothwell, P. M. (editor) (2007) *The Lancet: Treating Individuals. From randomised trials to personalised medicine.* Elsevier.

(15) Christensen, C. M., Grossman, J. H. and Hwang, J. (2009) *The Innovator's Prescription. A Disruptive Solution for Health Care.* McGraw-Hill Professional.

(16) Simon, H. A. (1957) A Behavioural Model of Rational Choice. In *Models of Man, Social and Rational: Mathematical Essays on Rational Human Behaviour in a Social Setting.* Wiley.

(17) Gigerenzer, G., Todd, P. M. and the ABC Research Group (1999) *Simple Heuristics That Make Us Smart.* Oxford University Press Inc.

(18) Gawande, A. (2003) *Complications: A Surgeon's Notes on an Imperfect Science.* Profile Books Ltd.

(19) Groopman, J. (2007) *How Doctors Think.* Houghton Mifflin Harcourt.

(20) Berlin, I. (1958) *Two Concepts of Liberty. An Inaugural Lecture delivered before the University of Oxford on 31 October 1958.* [Pamphlet] The Clarendon Press, Oxford.

(21) Rothman, D. J. (1997) *Beginnings Count. The Technological Imperative in American Health Care.* Oxford University Press, USA.

(22) Degner, L. F., Kristjanson, L. J., Bowman, D., Sloan, J. A., Carriere, K. C., O'Neil, J., Bilodeau, B., Watson, P. and Mueller, B. (1997) Information needs and decisional preferences in women with breast cancer. *JAMA* 277: 1485–1492.

(23) Cox, K., Britten, N., Hooper, R. and White, P. (2007) Patients' involvement in decisions about medicines: GPs' perceptions of their preferences. *Br. J. Gen. Pract.* 57: 777–784.

(24) Gray, J. A. M. (2002) *The Resourceful Patient.* eRosetta Press, Oxford.

(25) Henegan, C., Alonso-Coello, P., Garcia-Alamino, J. M., Perera, R., Meats, E. and Glasziou, P. (2006) Self-monitoring of oral anticoagulation: a systematic review and meta-analysis. *Lancet* 367; 404–411.

5

HOW TO BUILD A HEALTHCARE SYSTEM

This chapter will:

- introduce the concepts of objectives, criteria, and standards when applied to healthcare systems;
- discuss different levels at which systems can be focused;
- describe the Map of Medicine®, and how it can be used to display pathways.

By the end of the chapter, you will have developed an understanding of:

- how to set objectives for a system;
- the main advantages and disadvantages of using process and outcome criteria;
- how to choose standards for different levels of quality.

Touchstone: The health service as the *Titanic*

According to the US inquiry into the sinking [of the Titanic*], Mr Fleet recalled seeing Mr Blair with binoculars during the trip from Belfast to Southampton. Asked where Mr Blair's glasses went, Mr Fleet replied: 'We do not know. We only know we never got a pair.'*

Senator Smith, the chairman of the inquiry, said: 'Suppose you had glasses . . . could you have seen this black object [at] a greater distance?'

Fleet: 'We could have seen it a bit sooner.'

Smith: 'How much sooner?'

Fleet: 'Well, enough to get out of the way.'

> *Smith: 'Were you disappointed that you had no glasses?'*
> *Fleet: 'Yes, sir.'*
>> Extract from a report in *The Daily Telegraph*,
>> 29 August 2007
>
> Generating healthcare information is like the wake produced by a ship as it moves forwards. The wake of the *Titanic* appeared perfect until it was realised all too late that the ship was following the wrong course to avoid mishap. A service needs to look forwards as well as backwards, and designing systems helps everyone involved to do that.

How to set the framework for a healthcare system

In this section, a framework for a healthcare system is set out, together with instructions for working with system stakeholders to identify:

- The aim of a system;
- The objectives for the system, and its outcomes;
- The criteria to measure whether system objectives are being met;
- The standards against which performance can be compared.

How to choose the focus for a healthcare system

Systems can have as a focus various aspects of ill health and its management, as follows:

- symptoms or clinical presentations, such as chest pain or suspected stroke;
- diseases or clinical conditions, such as epilepsy or bipolar disorder;
- complex challenges, such as older people who have multiple health and social care needs and are at risk of admission to long-term care;
- the process of care, such as a safer prescribing system.

However, the purpose of this book is primarily to describe the types of healthcare system that serve populations or groups of people with a common need (disease) which requires a well-coordinated and systematic response.

How to set the aim for a healthcare system

Every system needs an aim. An aim is a single, high-level statement of purpose, essential for vision and focus. It should be written:

- with boldness;
- as a simple memorable sentence;
- to focus on the outcome.

The aim should also be inspirational, for example: 'To help people with epilepsy live a full life'.

When the NHS Breast Screening Programme was set up, its aim was 'To reduce mortality from breast cancer'. However, such an explicit aim had inherent problems.

1. The existence of many confounding factors meant that if mortality were to be reduced the reduction could be attributed to other factors – this happened; conversely, if mortality was not reduced due to the influence of other factors, the programme could be deemed ineffective – this also happened.
2. The aim was insufficient for the task of managing the NHS Breast Screening Programme. Years would need to elapse before any decrease in mortality could be measured, and in the meantime those responsible for managing services would have no indication from changes in the mortality rate that problems with delivery existed in one or more of the constituent services. To manage a system, a set of more detailed objectives is needed to amplify the aim.

How to gain ownership of the aim

The aim of a system should be agreed by all the stakeholders involved in system development.

- Draft the aim as a single sentence that could fit onto a T-shirt.
- Invite as many stakeholders involved in the programme's activities as you can, ensuring that there are at least two participants from each of the activities, and that patients and carers are represented as well as professionals. Explain why systems are important, and show participants the table that will eventually form the basis of the integrated system of care (Figure 5.1).

Aim					
Objectives	Criteria	Outcome		Standards	
			Minimal acceptable	Achievable	Excellent

Figure 5.1 The framework for an integrated system of care

- Circulate, or show on a screen, the draft aim of the system.
- Ask stakeholders to reflect on each word of the aim, as well as on the sentence as a whole.
- Ask each person to find someone they do not normally work with or, preferably, they have never met, introduce themselves, and spend three minutes discussing the wording of the aim.
- Take feedback and, according to responses, amend the aim, going through it word by word.
- Tell stakeholders that it might take as many as five iterations to agree the system aim.
- In addition, ask stakeholders to think of a single outcome measure that could be used to assess whether the system has achieved its aim. As an example, the desired outcome of a Fetal Risk Assessment Programme would not be the number of terminations undertaken, but the number and percentage of women who had been able to make an informed choice about the results of fetal risk assessment.

How to define the scope of a system

It is essential to define the set of activities that need to be coordinated through the system; this is known as the 'scope'. The scope of any system should be as wide as necessary to include every activity relevant to the aim. The extent of the scope should not be constrained by the fact that one or more of the activities:

- are not under the managerial control of the team leading the development of the system;
- appear to have no-one responsible for managing them.

For example, the scope of a system for Fetal Risk Assessment needs to include biochemistry, ultrasound, genetics, gynaecology for amniocentesis, pathology, information technology, and counselling and communication.

The exercise of agreeing the set of activities helps to clarify the scope and title of the system. For example, the scope of a 'cancer *control* programme' would include activities such as smoking cessation and screening, whereas the scope of a 'cancer *care* programme' would not. The set of activities involved in breast screening are displayed in Table 2.1, each identified on the basis that they would contribute to achieving the aim of the NHS Breast Screening Programme.

Although the extent of the scope needs to be wider than the contribution of a single service, it does not need to include everything. For example, in discussion about the scope of a system for chronic obstructive pulmonary disease (COPD), the question was raised: 'Should we include smoking cessation and end-of-life care?' The consensus was that this would be too broad a scope, and that:

- smoking cessation should be considered as part of a system for disease prevention;
- end-of-life care for people with COPD was little different from that for people with other diseases, and end-of-life care should be considered as a system in its own right.

How to define the objectives of a system

Although a system requires an overarching aim, there are several weaknesses associated with the establishment of a high-level aim in isolation, however important that aim might be.

- It can take many years for an aim to be achieved or realised, but the people responsible for managing systems need information as feedback over a much shorter time period.
- If the aim is not being achieved, it is essential to identify which parts of the system require modification because all may not be equally at fault.

For these reasons, every system needs a set of objectives. Indeed, without objectives there is no system.

Objectives are lower level statements of purpose. They are more useful for management purposes than an aim because progress against objectives can be measured at regular intervals, ranging from each day to every year. Peter Drucker has defined the purpose of objectives, as follows.

Objectives are needed in every area where performance and results directly and vitally affect the survival and prosperity of the business. . . . Objectives should enable us to do five things:
1. *to organize and explain the whole range of business pheno-mena in a small number of general statements;*
2. *to test these statements in actual experience;*
3. *to predict behaviour;*
4. *to appraise the soundness of decisions when they are still being made;*
5. *to enable practising business men to analyse their own experience and, as a result, improve their performance.* (1)

Wittgenstein said that every idea is a picture. Although the action of setting objectives is a critical step in building a system, it is good to have two pictures in mind before starting on the detail.

1. The first picture is the system as a set of activities with a feedback loop and a regular flow of new knowledge. The closed healthcare system in Figure 2.1 is rare. Even central heating is an open system,

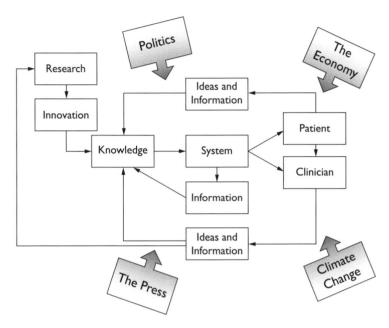

Figure 5.2 An open healthcare system with feedback

affected for instance by people leaving windows open. Health services are open systems, influenced deliberately by research and policy, and inadvertently by outside events such as global economic crises or shocks (see Figure 5.2).

2. The second picture is the system as a table, see Figure 5.3 in which as an example the objectives for an epilepsy service are presented in the first column.

The original set of objectives for the NHS Breast Screening Programme is shown in Table 2.1.

Types of objectives

It is possible to group objectives into two different types:

- those that focus on activity relating to the patients or population served, i.e. that are clinically orientated, for instance:
  - To diagnose epilepsy quickly and accurately;

Objectives	Criteria	Standards
To diagnose epilepsy quickly and accurately		
To treat effectively and with minimal side-effects		
To help the child and their family to adjust to the diagnosis and to minimise handicap		
To ensure that the child with epilepsy and other problems receives prompt and comprehensive assessment		
To involve children and their families, both individually and collectively in disease management		
To promote and support research		
To develop all the professionals and practitioners involved in epilepsy care		
To make the best use of resources		
To produce an annual report for the population served		

Figure 5.3 Setting objectives – a critical step in building a system

- To treat epilepsy effectively and with minimal side-effects;
- those concerned with managerial issues, for example:
  - To make the best use of resources.

Managerial objectives also allow statements of principle to be voiced. Objectives such as 'To promote and support research' and 'To develop all the professionals and practitioners involved in epilepsy care' remind all those who work in, manage, or fund the programme that functions such as research and staff development are equal in status to activities described in objectives that focus on patients or the population. Although a system of care can operate for some weeks or months without research or staff development, it cannot continue to do so for years.

If managerial issues are included during objective-setting, they should be covered in the annual report.

Conflicting objectives

Objectives can sometimes conflict with one another, or at least be in mutual tension. The objective in the NHS Breast Screening Programme that encourages and promotes the identification of cancers can lead to attempts to increase the programme's sensitivity, that is, the number of cancers identified. However, the consequence of increasing sensitivity is that many more women are deemed to have a 'positive' mammogram at the expense of the programme's specificity, that is, the number of women who are told they might have cancer but who are eventually cleared. As a decrease in specificity increases the amount of anxiety created by the programme, the objective focused on improved diagnosis is in conflict with the objective of minimising anxiety.

How to gain ownership of the objectives

The objectives of a system should be agreed by all the stakeholders involved in integrated system development. One way of gaining ownership of the objectives for a system is set out below.

- Invite stakeholders involved in the programme's activities, ensuring that there are at least two participants from each of the activities, and that patients and carers are represented as well as professionals. It is ideal if the same participants that were involved in developing the aim for the system are involved in developing the objectives; alternatively you might be able to do both exercises at the same meeting.
- Circulate, or show on a screen, a set of objectives for another clinical system. You could use the set for epilepsy on page 96 or those for breast screening in Table 2.1. Highlight the two different types of objective – clinically and management orientated. Ask the whole group if there are any outstanding omissions.
- Now circulate a draft set of objectives for their programme. Tell the

group there should be no more than 10 objectives: if they want to add one, they need to delete another. Depending on the time available, you can do a two-minute brainstorm with feedback on:
- the whole set of objectives;
- the clinically orientated and the management-orientated subsets; *or*
- each objective, one by one.

How to select criteria

Each objective needs to have one or more criteria associated with it in order to measure progress. Without criteria, objectives are meaningless.

Several terms are used as synonyms for criteria: 'metrics', 'indicators', or 'measures'. Some people use the term 'measures' to mean criteria that are considered to be of greater validity than indicators, for example, they would use the term 'measure' about systematic surveys of patient experience, whereas they would use the word 'indicator' for the number of letters of complaint or commendation that a hospital Chief Executive receives. Although the latter is less costly, it is less valuable in terms of feedback for the system than the accurate measures used in the former.

A. J. Ayer in his book, *Language, Truth and Logic,* proposed a 'principle of verification', based on the work of the philosophers in the Vienna Circle:

> *Instead of trying to understand the meaning of a proposition by analysing the meaning of the individual words that compose it, another approach should be taken. The criterion which we use to test the genuineness of apparent statements of facts is the criterion of verifiability. We say that a sentence is factually significant to any given person if, and only if, he knows how to verify the proposition which it purports to express – that is, if he knows what observations will lead him, under certain conditions, to accept the proposition as being true, or reject it as being false. And with regard to questions, the procedure is the same. We enquire in every case what observations will lead us to answer the question one way or the other, and, if none can be*

*discovered, we must conclude that the sentence under con-
sideration does not, as far as we are concerned, express a genuine
question, however strongly its grammatical appearance may
suggest that it does.* (2)

The trade-off between validity and feasibility

When selecting criteria, the most important issue to tackle is the trade-
off between their validity and feasibility (and cost) of collecting the
data. Validity is the degree to which a criterion measures what it is
intended to measure; feasibility is the ease with which the information
can be collected. In general, the greater the validity of a measure, the
greater the cost to collect it. In the course of designing an information
subsystem to underpin a healthcare system, the aim must be to build
the required data into the routine data collection process. For
instance, at Dartmouth–Hitchcock Medical Center, there is a well-
developed information subsystem where patient preferences are
routinely recorded, as is the type of treatment given to patients. It is
then possible to compare the treatment received with stated preference to identify whether patients' preferences are being met.

How to gain ownership of the criteria

The same group of people who set the objectives for a system can also
be involved in selecting criteria. In addition, it is useful to invite
others, such as academics, who can bring rigour to pinpointing
definitions and the meaning of specific criteria. It may be necessary
to set up a subgroup to address the issues associated with selecting
appropriate criteria. For example, when drawing up criteria for a
screening programme, reaching consensus on the definition of an
'interval cancer' could take considerable time.

- Invite as many stakeholders involved in the programme's activities
  as you can, ensuring that there are at least two participants from
  each of the activities, and that patients and carers are represented as
  well as professionals.
- As a warm-up, ask participants to work in pairs and choose criteria
  for an objective completely unrelated to the clinical system under

development: e.g. a criminological system with the objective 'To reduce not only crime but also the fear of crime', or an educational system with the objective 'To produce children who are good citizens'.

- During feedback about the warm-up question, introduce the concepts of validity and feasibility as applied to criteria.
- Circulate the objectives for the system.
- Inform participants that the most important ground rule is not to worry whether the criteria they identify can be measured from the data currently being collected; when the criteria have been selected, the specification for data collection can then be prepared for the people developing the information technology and record subsystems.
- Be prepared to go through each objective one by one – it may take a long time for participants to select criteria.
- For each objective, ask people to discuss in pairs the data they would need to be able to decide whether the objective was being met. Remind them that they must not think about the data currently being collected.
- During feedback, it is possible that the first suggestion made is valid and feasible, but this usually takes some time and the discussion could last as long as an hour.

To support stakeholders during this exercise, it can be useful to have:

1. Research reports about the condition being discussed – the outcome used in the research may have the potential to be adopted or adapted;
2. A person who is experienced in framing research questions and designing research protocols, even if they have not undertaken research on the particular disease or condition for which the system is being designed.

When a new system is being created, the tendency is for people to identify what are known as structural criteria. For instance, when setting up a system to provide high-quality care for children with epilepsy, structural criteria might include:

- the recruitment of a specialist paediatric neurologist;

- establishing a parents' group to provide feedback to the service;
- instituting five-day cover from a trained educational psychologist.

These are known as 'all-or-none' criteria, where the criteria describe a resource that is either present or absent. Such criteria are useful when setting up a service, but once a service is in place they are of relatively little use. If statements like this are made by stakeholders, they make explicit and highlight that a paediatric epilepsy service needs a specially trained paediatric neurologist, and the presence of that specialist defines whether the system exists.

However, when measuring performance, it is better to select criteria that will highlight whether there is variation in either process or outcomes for patients, for example:

- the percentage of children with epilepsy who have had a full neurological assessment – this is a process measure;
- the percentage of children with epilepsy who have had no fits during the course of the year – this is an outcome measure.

Using process and outcome criteria, it is possible to track the performance of a service over time, or compare it with that of other services. The key issue when choosing criteria for healthcare management in times of resource and other constraints is the relative contribution of criteria that measure process and those that measure outcome. It would be ideal to have a process and an outcome criterion for each objective, but usually process measures are easier to collect, and therefore they score highly on feasibility, but they have less validity than outcome criteria.

How to define outcomes

Outcome is an elusive concept, beset with many meanings. Avedis Donabedian was the first to distinguish between the structure, process and outcome of care (3), and his definitions are quoted in the White Paper, *Equity and Excellence: Liberating the NHS* (4) (see Box 5.1).

Although Donabedian's definitions have stood the test of time, there have been several developments in the use of the term outcome:

- the distinction between primary and secondary outcomes;
- the increasing use of intermediate outcomes.

Box 5.1: Donabedian's definitions of the structures, processes and outcomes of care

- The structures of care – based on robust evidence: how should treatment and care be structured in order to maximise the chance of a good outcome for the patient?
- The processes of care – based on robust evidence: what are the things that should be done to maximise the chance of a good outcome for the patient?
- The outcomes of care – what actually happens to the health of the patient, the outcome, as a result of the treatment and care they receive?

A primary outcome is defined as the real objective of treatment. For example, the primary outcome of a heart disease prevention programme is the incidence of heart attacks; a secondary outcome is defined as a change in a risk factor, such as blood pressure levels.

However, although the primary outcome of a heart disease prevention programme can be measured according to the incidence of heart attacks, there are two problems with using such an outcome measure.

1. It may take years and a very large population for any changes to become manifest, and so intermediate outcomes may have to be chosen – for a heart disease prevention programme, an intermediate outcome would be changes in the blood lipid levels of the population being studied
2. It may be affected by many factors other than the health service providing care, as described by Julian Le Grand.

   There is a particular problem with outcomes, in that it is often difficult to attribute a given outcome improvement (such as in the health of a patient) to a particular item of public service (such as a course of medical treatment). For the outcome may in large part be due to a variety of factors that are not within the control of the providers of the service concerned (such as the patient's own recuperative powers). This is one of the reasons why, although both providers and policy makers often pay lip service to the importance of outcomes, in practice they usually give more attention to factors that are more under the control of the service, such as inputs, processes and outputs. (5)

It is clear that both process and outcome measures have a part to play in measuring performance, as the White Paper states.

At a national level the focus and accountability should, as far as possible, be centred around the outcomes of care. Locally, the structures and processes of care will need to be monitored but focusing on these too heavily at a national level can lead to a distortion of clinical priorities and risks creating a whole system of accountability that is more concerned with the means than the result – an accountability system that has lost sight of the purpose of the NHS. (4)

In theory, setting objectives, choosing criteria and defining outcomes might seem to be a straightforward linear process, but the reality is different (see Figure 5.4). When defining outcomes, it may become clear that the criteria chosen to measure progress and/or the wording of an objective need to be reconsidered and changed.

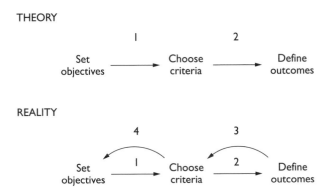

Figure 5.4 Recursive development of objectives, criteria, and standards

Setting the framework for an integrated system of care for chronic obstructive pulmonary disease

If the aim of a chronic obstructive pulmonary disease (COPD) system is 'To help people with COPD live a fulfilling life', one objective would be 'To treat patients with COPD safely and effectively'. The criteria for this objective are shown in Display 5.1 below.

Display 5.1

Objective	Criteria
To treat patients with COPD safely and effectively	• pCO_2 measurements of the amount of carbon dioxide in the bloodstream • patients' reports on how they feel • patients' reports on whether they experienced side-effects • clinical findings of side-effects and errors

However, for each of the criteria associated with an objective, it is essential to record in separate columns, as shown in Display 5.2, the terms used to define:

- the outcome for the individual patient;
- the outcome for the service, that is, when the outcomes for the individual patient are added together for the whole population.

It is only for the last 10 years that a patient's experience of the humanity of their treatment and care has been considered an outcome of importance equal to that of clinical effectiveness. Lord Darzi can take much of the credit for that in England. However, in the example for COPD, patients' reports are essential to measuring not only emotional experience but also the clinical effectiveness of treatment. This has led to the development of patient reported outcomes measures, known as PROMs.

> The umbrella term Patient Reported Outcomes (PRO) has been successfully proposed for instruments measuring perceived health outcomes. (6)

To generate useful and usable information, outcomes for the service need to be interpreted in relation to a set of standards.

Display 5.2

Objective	Criteria	Outcome for the individual patient	Outcome for the service
To treat patients with COPD safely and effectively	pCO_2 measurements of the amount of carbon dioxide in the bloodstream	$pCO_2 = x$, which could be lower or higher than before the start of treatment, or the same	Distribution of pCO_2 levels for all the patients
	Patients' reports about how they feel	Patient reports whether they feel: • better; • no better; • worse	Number and percentage feeling: • better; • no better; • worse
	Patients' reports about whether they experienced side-effects	Patient reports: • no concern about harmful effects of treatment; • effects they believe to be harmful	Number and percentage of patients reporting: • no concerns; • concerns about possible harms of treatment
	Clinical findings of side-effects and errors	Record in individual patient's notes about treatment side-effects or errors	Percentage of patients with recorded side-effects or errors

How to set standards

Having formulated objectives and chosen criteria to measure those objectives, the next stage in the development of a system is to set standards. (Standards can be set for process criteria even in the absence of outcomes.)

Donabedian, in many ways the founder of the healthcare quality movement, said in a lecture that '*the quality of a health service is the degree to which it conforms to pre-set standards of goodness*'.

When setting standards, it is important to be aware that standards are subjective, and different perspectives exist. A manager may think a service is of good quality, but patients and carers may regard its quality as poor, or vice versa. Many people rate their experience with alternative or complementary medicine as high in quality, whereas many clinicians would regard the service provided as low in value.

The standards to be achieved for the COPD service are set out in Display 5.3.

Display 5.3

Outcome for the service	*Standard to be achieved*
Distribution of pCO_2 levels for all the patients	More than 70% of patients having had a reduction in pCO_2 measurement since diagnosis
Number and percentage feeling: • better; • no better; • worse	More than 80% of patients reporting feeling better since starting treatment
Number and percentage reporting: • no concerns; • concerns about possible harms of treatment.	Less than 10% of patients reporting concerns about possible adverse effects of treatment
Percentage of patients with recorded side-effects or errors	Less than 5% of records showing evidence of side-effects or errors

It is often useful to set more than one level of standard. In a book popular in the 1990s entitled *In Search of Excellence* (7), people were exhorted to be excellent. However, exhortations to excellence can be de-motivating to people working in difficult circumstances aware that excellence is the result not only of hard work but often of the chance coalition of skilful individuals working in a propitious environment. For this reason, it is advisable to set three levels of standard:

- a minimal acceptable standard, below which no programme of care should fall;
- an excellent standard, which is reached by the best; and

- an achievable standard.

However, determining the level of achievability for a standard can also be subjective. One approach is to take the cut-off point between the top quartile and the remaining three-quarters of services. Using this approach, it is possible for programmes in the bottom quartile operating in difficult circumstances, such as inner city areas, to take as a benchmark an inner city programme that comes in the top quartile, rather than the excellent standard reached by the best services. This approach allows programmes in the bottom quartile to identify with other programmes providing services to a population similar to their own. Irrespective of the achievable standard, any programme in the top quartile can aim for excellence, and it is to be expected that all programmes will improve over time.

When setting standards, it is helpful if performance measures are already available. If performance data are available for all the programmes, they can be visualised as a histogram, statistical control chart or distribution chart. Such visualisations of performance data make it easier to identify thresholds for the minimal acceptable and achievable standards; using Figure 5.5, the percentage of patients in England admitted to hospital following a stroke who spend 90% of their time on a stroke unit, an achievable standard of 75% could be set, representing the cut-off point between the top quintile of primary care trusts and the rest. In the absence of performance data, it is more difficult to set the minimal acceptable and achievable standards, but experience (people's tacit knowledge) and research evidence can be used as a basis instead.

How to set standards for a new service when there are no performance data

When setting standards at the inception of a service, it is necessary to utilise both experience and research data. Research papers often describe excellence, and although achieving excellence may seem daunting it is helpful to be aware of excellent services when setting the standards for a new service.

- Collect any research papers relevant to service quality.
- Invite as many stakeholders involved in the programme's activities

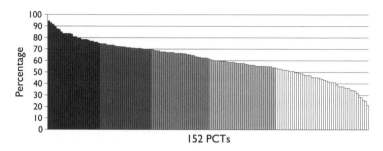

Figure 5.5 Percentage of patients admitted to hospital following a stroke who spend 90% of their time on a stroke unit by primary care trust (PCT) in England (2009/10)

as you can, ensuring that there are at least two participants from each of the activities, and that patients and carers are represented as well as professionals.

- Circulate the research papers to participants before the meeting.
- Ensure that all participants have a copy of the objectives for the service.
- Ask participants to discuss the level of service provision that they would regard as the minimum below which any service should not be allowed to fall, representing the minimal acceptable standard. Often, when setting standards for a new service, people concentrate on the structural elements that need to be in place, for example, 'Each programme must have an identified coordinator', but the focus needs to be on the process of care. To help participants focus on process rather than structural elements, ask them to think of the service when it is already in operation. Another way to stimulate appropriate responses to this task is to encourage participants to write the first annual report for the service before it has been established.
- Using the research findings circulated beforehand, ask participants to identify the level of performance that the service should seek to attain – the achievable standard. If the performance level achieved by the researchers is thought to be a level of excellence unlikely to be achieved by any service immediately, a lower level of performance can be selected as the achievable standard.

Thus, for each objective, it is possible using a combination of information from research and experience to identify a minimal acceptable standard, below which the service should not fall, and an achievable standard which the service should reasonably be expected to attain.

How to set standards for a service already in operation

When services are already in operation, it is possible to base standard-setting on performance data.

- Plot the performance measures for each individual service, and look at the distribution of the performance measures for all the services.
- Ask the stakeholders for each service, including managers: 'What is the level below which no service should fall?' It is possible that stakeholders will define a level for the minimal acceptable standard which all services have already exceeded, although this would not be very challenging. Alternatively, the average for all services could be regarded as the minimal acceptable standard. However, this would cause chaos because it is always necessary to mount an investigation if a service is below the minimal acceptable standard; some people would argue that such services should be suspended. Another approach is to ascertain the performance level for the bottom 10% of services, and suggest that this level should be chosen as the minimal acceptable standard, giving those services in the bottom 10% one year to reach it.
- Ask participants to look at the distribution curve and identify the standard every service could reasonably be expected to achieve, representing the achievable standard. Point out it is rarely sensible to choose the standard set by the best, but instead to select a cut-off point, such as the value that differentiates the top quartile of services from the rest, in order to define an achievable standard

Target-setting

The clear advice from John Seddon is 'Don't set targets.' Seddon's book on *Systems Thinking in the Public Sector* (8) is a powerful attack on what he calls 'deliverology', and the target culture. Plucking targets from the air leads to a variety of different responses, as Edwards Deming has identified (9):

- numbers are fiddled to achieve the target;
- work is fiddled to make it fit the targets;
- only a few people actually meet the targets.

Target-setting as an approach is often linked to payment by results. Although payment by results has certain benefits, there is almost always a disadvantage, described by Bob Wachter as '*the unexpected consequences of the quality and IT revolution*' (10). Target-setting can lead people to focus only on those issues that have been prioritised, and they tend to ignore everything else. Although target-setting can have a part to play in improvement, there are likely to be unintended consequences unless the relevant team has been closely involved in identifying the targets, and they are set within a framework of aim, objectives, criteria, outcomes, and standards (Figure 5.6). If workers set their own targets, they can be overly ambitious, and may need help to ensure that any targets set are appropriate.

Aim				
Objective	Criteria	Outcome	Standards	Target for improvement (if any)

Figure 5.6 **Relationship between targets for improvement and the aim, objectives, criteria, outcomes and standards of a system**

Another argument against targets is outlined by Alfie Kohn in *Punished by Rewards. The Trouble with Gold Stars, Incentive Plans, A's, Praise and Other Bribes* (11), which covers not only healthcare but also the education and raising of children. Kohn emphasises the problems that can arise from target-setting and giving rewards, including a failure to motivate people, and the potential to *reduce* the level of motivation.

Producing the annual report

For the person responsible for managing or paying for a system of care, a better approach is to compare the system with explicit standards and to measure progress against the benchmarks set by those standards. That said, it is possible for individual professionals, teams, or services to identify targets in order to set a challenge for themselves, and gain a sense of achievement. By comparing the outcome with the standard for each objective, it is possible to identify which of the objectives are not being achieved and to take action on the relevant activities.

The results should be presented in an annual report written for the intelligent lay person as well as for the service users. Choosing a lay person as one of the target readers has several advantages:

- it forces the author(s) to be clear about the definition of terms, such as 'prevalence' (a term that many professionals are also unsure about);
- readers could include people who have the condition but who have not been referred to the service despite the fact that they would benefit from it.

In the 21st century, every service and each clinician needs to be aware of the population they serve in addition to their commitment to the individual patients they see. Mark Friedman, in his book *Trying Hard Is Not Good Enough: How to Produce Measurable Improvements for Customers and Communities*, emphasises the need to be accountable to the population (population accountability) as well as to the service users, who are interested in its performance (performance accountability) (12). There is an overlap between these two types of accountability measure, but there are distinct differences in emphasis as illustrated in Table 5.1 (12).

Table 5.1 Accountability questions for populations and service users (12)

The 7 accountability questions for populations	*The 7 accountability questions for service users*
• What are the quality of life conditions we want for our children, adults and families who live in our community? • What would those conditions look like if we could see them? • How can we measure those conditions? • How are we doing on the most important of these measures? • Who are the partners that have a role to play in doing better? • What works to do better, including no-cost and low-cost ideas? • What do we propose to do?	• Who are our customers? • How can we measure if our customers are better off? • How can we measure if we are delivering services well? • How are we doing on the most important of these measures? • Who are the partners that have a role to play in doing better? • What works to do better, including no-cost and low-cost ideas? • What do we propose to do?

The implications of the imperative to increase transparency and accountability to the population served will have a major influence on both the way in which clinicians work, and the way in which they are educated. This is discussed in detail in a companion book in this series entitled *How To Practise Population Medicine*.

If you don't have an annual report, you don't have a service.

Questions for reflection when teaching or developing networks
If using these questions during network building or teaching, ask the group to work in pairs and reflect on one of the questions for three minutes; try to get people who do not know one another to work together.

When taking feedback, let each pair make only one point. In the interests of equity, if you start with the pair on the left-hand side of the room for the first question, start with the pair on the right-hand side of the room for the second question.

- What are the advantages and disadvantages of using process measures when compared with using outcome measures?
- The three levels of standard described in this chapter are minimal acceptable, achievable, and excellent. What other adjectives are used or could be used to describe different levels of quality?
- When designing a localised system from a national guideline, how much should local views and opinions be allowed to influence the tests and treatments in the pathway?

References

(1) Drucker, P. F. (1955) *The Practice of Management.* William Heinemann.
(2) Ayer, A. J. (1936) *Language, Truth and Logic.* Victor Gollancz.
(3) Donabedian, A. (1966) Evaluating the Quality of Medical Care. *The Milbank Memorial Fund Quarterly* 44; 166–203.
(4) Department of Health (2010) *Equity and Excellence: Liberating the NHS.* Available at: http://www.dh.gov.uk/en/Publicationsand statistics/Publications/PublicationsPolicyAndGuidance/DH_117353
(5) Le Grand, J. (2007) *The Other Invisible Hand. Delivering Public Services through Choice and Competition.* Princeton University Press.
(6) Valderas, J. M. and Alonso, J. (2008) Patient reported outcome measures: a model-based classification system for research and clinical practice. *Qual. Life Res.* 17: 1125. doi: 10.1007/s11136-008-9396-4.
(7) Peters, T. and Waterman, R. H. (1995) *In Search of Excellence: Lessons from America's Best-Run Companies.* HarperCollins.
(8) Seddon, J. (2008) *Systems Thinking in the Public Sector. The failure of the reform regime . . . and a manifesto for a better way.* Triarchy Press.

(9) Deming, W. E. (1986) *Out of the Crisis.* McGraw-Hill.

(10) Wachter, R. M. (2006) Expected and unanticipated consequences of the quality and information technology revolutions. *JAMA* 295; 2780–2782.

(11) Kohn, A. (2000) *Punished by Rewards. The Trouble with Gold Stars, Incentive Plans, A's, Praise and Other Bribes.* Houghton Mifflin.

(12) Friedman, M. (2005) *Trying Hard is Not Good Enough. How to Produce Measurable Improvements for Customers and Communities.* Trafford Publishing.

6

HOW ARE HEALTHCARE SYSTEMS BEST MANAGED?

This chapter will:

- discuss how systems can compete;
- introduce the taxonomy of different types of network;
- discuss sapiential authority, and the contribution of knowledge to system management.

By the end of this chapter you will have developed an understanding of:

- how to run a health service in which the principal focus, including the focus of competition, is on systems and not institutions;
- the different styles of managing networks;
- the contribution that information technology can make to the management of a system.

Touchstone: The health service as anthill

Ants could claim to be the most successful species. It is true they have not invented the hula hoop or the Mini, neither have they been to the moon, but they are ubiquitous and thriving. Their success is built on cooperation and competition – they cooperate with each other in their own colony, but compete, if necessary, with other colonies. They do not have a strong bureaucracy; the queen is not the Chief Executive. Neither do they use the market as we would recognise it, but they work together for the common good.

In 2009, the Nobel Prize for Economic Sciences was awarded jointly to Oliver E. Williamson, for demonstrating that the transaction costs of both markets and bureaucracies were no longer justified by increased value (1), and Elinor Ostrom for her work on social organisation, *Governing the Commons: The Evolution of Institutions for Collective Action* (2).

Ostrom argues that people are not necessarily selfish, and will not exploit a common wealth, such as a river, meadow, or health service, if the system of governance is right.

> *Since Garrett Hardin's challenging article in* Science *(1968, page 1,244), the expression 'the tragedy of the commons' has come to symbolize the degradation of the environment to be expected whenever many individuals use a scarce resource in common. To illustrate the logical structure of his model, Hardin asks the reader to envision a pasture 'open to all'. He then examines the structure of this situation from the perspective of a rational herder. Each herder receives a direct benefit from his own animals and suffers delayed costs from the deterioration of the commons when his and others' cattle overgraze. Each herder is motivated to add more and more animals because he receives the direct benefit of his own animals and bears only a share of the costs resulting from overgrazing. Hardin concludes: 'Therein is the tragedy. Each man is locked into a system that compels him to increase his herd without limit – in a world that is limited. Ruin is the destination toward which all men rush, each pursuing his own best interest in a society that believes in the freedom of the commons.' (2)*

In their Pulitzer Prize-winning book *The Ants* (3), Bert Hölldobler and E. O. Wilson emphasise that one of the reasons ants are successful is that they work in networks, and can be regarded as altruistic. Given the right context, people will be altruistic too, and work together for the common good.

Systems, like any organism, have checks and balances. Information provides feedback allowing self-regulation.

A healthcare system does not need a Chief Executive or a Board, and may not even need its own budget. The development of a national Down's syndrome screening programme for England resulted in a consistent service being offered by about 45,000 clinicians, 150 ultrasound and antenatal services, 30 laboratories and 14 genetic laboratories to 600,000 pregnant women without:

- a single clinician being responsible in line-management terms to the screening programme; or
- the screening programme having a budget for the actual delivery of the screening services.

The national screening programme does have a budget for setting standards, for the management of the website, for training, and for the production of annual reports, but it does not directly employ any staff offering screening. Staff are employed by several hundred bureaucracies. The delivery of screening to the public does not have a ring-fenced screening budget; resources are managed by the same set of bureaucracies as employ the staff.

Although there are several reasons why setting up a system to manage screening was the preferred option, the main reason was that the delivery of healthcare is very complex, and to establish a budget for a single disorder would mean taking money from many other existing budgets. For instance, the establishment of a separate budget for a Down's syndrome screening programme would require contributions from at least seven other budgets (midwifery, laboratory services, imaging services, genetics, gynaecology, information systems, and education). Another difficulty is that the contribution of each of these services to Down's syndrome screening is interwoven with their contribution to many other clinical systems – the separation of the work done only for Down's syndrome would be no small task.

It is simpler for budgets to be managed by bureaucracies, and for systems to use knowledge to manage complex clinical processes. The results achieved by the small team managing the national newborn sickle cell screening programme have been outstanding but did not include bureaucratic control over all the services in the network (see Figure 6.1 for the most recent outcome measures).

Outcome	Criteria	Minimum standard (core)	Achievable standard (developmental)
Best possible survival for infants detected by the screening programme	Mortality rates expressed in person-years	Mortality rate in children under 5 of less than four per 1000 person-years of life (two deaths per 100 affected children)	Mortality rate in children under 5 of less than two per 1000 person-years of life (one death per 100 affected children)
Accurate detection of all infants born with major clinical significant abnormality	Sensitivity of the screening programme High quality newborn laboratory services	99% for HbSS 98% for HbSC 95% for other variants	99.5% for HbSS 99% for HbSC 97% for other variants

Figure 6.1 Outcomes, criteria and standards of the NHS Sickle Cell and Thalassaemia Screening Programme – newborn sickle cell screening (4)

It is true that one bureaucracy can be given the lead in coordinating the relationships among the different elements within a system, and it is always sensible to identify one person as the system coordinator or programme manager. The management of relationships can be time-consuming. Although some clinical time is necessary to provide clinical leadership, clinicians do not need to be involved in much of programme, or system, management. The programme manager is responsible for activities such as:

- communication;
- the development of training;
- the production of an annual report.

The programme manager does not have responsibility for the line management of other parts of the system, which may be in completely different bureaucracies, but is responsible for their coordination.

People running bureaucracies are sometimes nervous of the introduction of a systems approach because they feel that the lines of responsibility are not clear, particularly when things go wrong. However, this concern is unfounded.

1. If something goes wrong in one of the constituent services, then the line manager of that particular service is responsible.
2. If there is a problem in the relationship between two of the services that contribute to the system of care, then the programme manager's responsibility needs to be examined. If the programme manager has set up a clear mode of working between these two constituent services, and if measures to monitor whether relationships are working effectively are in place, then the programme manager cannot be held responsible when the system breaks down, although sometimes they are blamed.

Gandhi said '*A good system cannot make a bad man good*'. Thus, a system cannot mitigate for all the deficiencies of human nature and behaviour. A breakdown in relationships between separate services could be the responsibility of one or two of the service managers involved. Whenever a problem occurs within a system, it requires detailed examination.

How to use knowledge to manage systems

How to create knowledge-based systems

> *Toyota is a knowledge company.*
> Chairman of Toyota, *Singapore Daily News*, August 2008

All successful companies create, manage, and use knowledge as one of their highest priorities. Some successful companies, such as Bloomberg or Deloitte, produce nothing but knowledge: knowledge is the product their customers want. Other successful companies create, manage and use knowledge to generate and improve products. An excellent study by the Hitotsubashi Business School in Tokyo (5) and the book entitled *The Toyota Product Development System* (6) describe how Japanese companies, so often thought of as imitators, continually improve their offer to customers by creating new technology and new products using knowledge both from research and development and from experience to improve.

A knowledge-based system:

- creates networks and task-forces to complement their bureaucratic structure;
- captures and uses tacit knowledge;
- clarifies responsibility for knowledge;
- uses the power of information technology to create, distribute, manage, and use the three types of explicit generalisable knowledge (see below): knowledge from experience, knowledge from research, and knowledge from routinely collected or audit data.

A knowledge-based approach to service development is not achieved by bureaucratic re-organisation. Knowledge-based health services can be delivered by clinical networks. Any serious health problem is always managed by more than one bureaucracy, sometimes by as many as five.

A knowledge-based health service is a system that has the following components (not listed in any order of priority):

- a community of practice, which includes all relevant professionals, patients and groups;
- a set of objectives;
- a set of quality standards;
- a dataset made up of the criteria used to measure progress, together with data definitions for each criterion;
- an evidence base for professionals, with an annual evidence update;
- information primarily for patients, although patients should also have access to the evidence base;
- a website hosting all the relevant information – new research evidence, patient experience, and statistics relating to prescribing, hospital utilisation, and, if available, outcome;
- a shared space on the web for interactive working;
- a repository for locally produced documents;
- a quality improvement casebook, collecting and sharing the experience of professional staff;
- a specification for the information technology required to support the system – the information subsystem;
- care pathways expressed through the Map of Medicine®;
- one day a week of clinician time to coordinate the development of 'local' clinical networks.

Types of knowledge

There are two main types of knowledge – explicit and tacit knowledge.

- Tacit knowledge is knowledge derived from the experience of clinicians and patients; although this is a form of evidence, frequently it is not made available because no effort is made to capture or harvest it, a problem made worse by the increasing rate of staff turnover. It is necessary to convert tacit knowledge to explicit knowledge (Figure 6.2).
- There are two categories of explicit knowledge: particular and generalisable. Particular knowledge is relevant only to a particular patient, hospital or population; generalisable knowledge can be applied to patients, hospitals and populations other than those in which the knowledge was generated. There are three types of generalisable knowledge: knowledge derived from research, sometimes called evidence, knowledge from the analysis of routinely collected or audit data, sometimes called statistics or information, and knowledge from experience.

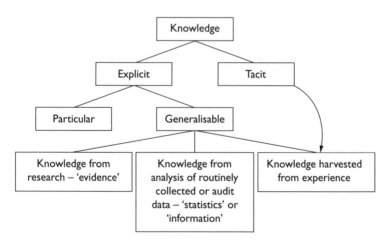

Figure 6.2 Conversion of tacit to explicit knowledge

The knowledge taxonomy

As Figure 6.2 shows, tacit knowledge has to be converted into explicit knowledge before it can become generalisable, and there are now excellent examples of how this can be done. For instance, in the book *Quality by Design*, the authors acknowledge the contribution of:

> . . . all the staff in the twenty clinical Microsystems that we studied, who taught us so much about what can be done to innovate and provide superior care. (7)

Systems are managed using sapiential authority, the authority that derives from knowledge, and not by bureaucratic authority, as described by Herbert Simon in his classic book, *Administrative Behavior. A Study of Decision-Making Processes in Administrative Organizations*:

> Authority: the concept of authority has been analyzed at length by students of administration. We shall employ here a definition substantially equivalent to that put forth by C. I. Barnard. A subordinate is said to accept authority whenever he permits his behaviour to be guided by the decision of a superior, without independently examining the merits of that decision. When exercising authority, the superior does not seek to convince the subordinate, but only to obtain his acquiescence. In actual practice, of course, authority is usually liberally admixed with suggestion and persuasion. (8)

A much shorter definition embracing sapiential authority is that of Amitai Etzioni:

> Authority, or legitimate power. (9)

Authority comes from knowledge, namely, the three types of explicit generalisable knowledge:

- evidence on benefits and harms;
- statistical information on system performance;
- experience about how to prevent and solve problems.

Managing all three types of knowledge requires one person to act as a coordinator, but it also requires the appropriate use of information technology.

Can systems compete?

It is possible for systems to compete. In *Redefining Health Care* (10), a review of the American healthcare dilemma, Porter and Teisberg concluded that competition between systems was the only type of competition worth debating. Porter, a world authority on competition in business, describes the problem of current comparisons. How is it possible to judge one hospital against another, one health maintenance organisation (HMO) against another, or one insurance fund against another? Although there can be competition between hospitals, the difficulty arises when a hospital with a good overall score may have some poor departments within it, and, conversely, when a hospital with a poor overall score has some excellent departments within it. Composite scores for hospitals are made up of some measures that are important to patients, and some measures that relate to amenities such as car parking. What patients are really interested in is the quality of a particular service set up to deal with their specific health problem. Hospital infection rates, which are common to all specialties, offer the concerned patient one way to avoid a hospital with high infection rates.

Fast forward to 2014: imagine what healthcare will be like then. You are a patient with inflammatory bowel disease living in Lincolnshire. You receive care from a system in which at least five bureaucracies are involved: your general practitioner, your pharmacy, your local hospital service, your local clinical commissioning group, and the teaching hospital at Nottingham, acting as the major node in the Three Counties Inflammatory Bowel Disease Service covering Derbyshire, Nottinghamshire and Lincolnshire. You download the annual report of the Three Counties Inflammatory Bowel Disease Service, and you note that they did 150 colon removal operations in Nottingham last year. As Lincolnshire is quite near to South Yorkshire, you look at the South Yorkshire Inflammatory Bowel Disease Service annual report. You see that Sheffield, the equivalent in the South Yorkshire service to Nottingham, only did five colon removal operations. Does that mean:

- Nottingham is very good at surgery?
- The South Yorkshire service is better at medical care, thus preventing the need for surgery?
- The threshold for surgery is too high in South Yorkshire?

Systems focusing on individual conditions are comparable; comparability is of central importance to competition. Condition-specific measures are clearly better than hospital-wide 'composite' measures when making comparisons about healthcare.

How strong is the evidence base for a systems approach?

There is evidence that a systems approach is effective, as exemplified by work at the Institute for Healthcare Improvement in the United States of America. The Institute's Founding Director, Don Berwick, emphasised the need to use a new approach to evaluating complex interventions such as the introduction of systems (11), notably the 'Realistic Evaluation' method of Ray Pawson and Nick Tilley (12).

In England, the NHS Breast Screening Programme was set up as a system with three main factors in its favour:

1. at that time, there was no screening taking place in England – the system was developed *de novo*, whereas the National Cervical Screening Programme had to be created out of chaos;
2. a central budget allowed a degree of control unusual in healthcare development;
3. a single team was given the responsibility and authority to implement policy.

As a benchmark, the team had the performance achieved in the Swedish randomised controlled trials during which the efficacy of breast screening had been demonstrated. It took five years for the mean performance of the English programme to reach this benchmark, and 10 years for the worst performing programme to reach it (13).

The NHS Breast Screening Programme demonstrates that it is possible to translate the efficacy achieved in a research setting to a level of effectiveness achievable in a routine service setting, provided that a systems approach is used (Figure 6.3).

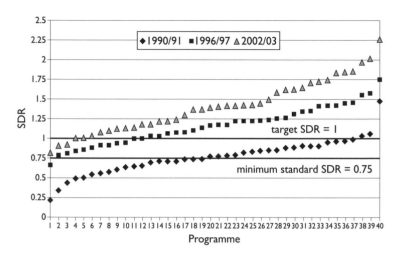

Figure 6.3 Quality improvement in the NHS Breast Screening Programme (13)

The literature on systems is not easy to access because the keyword for relevant papers might not be 'system', but 'network' or 'quality improvement'. In 2004, the results of a systematic literature review of networks by the NHS Service Delivery and Organisation R&D Programme were published as two documents (final and policy reports). (14) The work was part of a review of clinical networks in both the public and private sectors, focusing on network structure, management, and governance.

The literature on networks has grown substantially since then. One common theme is the location of power and authority within a network, and how much independence and control network members have. This can be depicted as a spectrum ranging from networks that exist within a pure market to networks that exist within a pure hierarchy (Figure 6.4). There are three main types of network corresponding to the different levels of control given to network members:

- an equal partner network;
- a coordinated network;
- a dominated network.

125

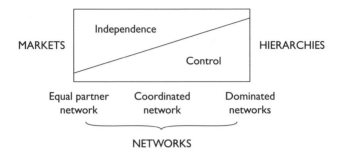

Figure 6.4 The market-hierarchy spectrum in relation to different
types of network

The dominated network

In a dominated network, one member is dominant, and other members, usually smaller in size, are dependent upon it. The dominated network is common in industry, exemplified by large businesses that outsource much of the production process to other companies, who act as suppliers.

The dominated network was pioneered in Japan, where powerful players such as Toyota developed long-term relationships with the suppliers of components, who learned to appreciate the dominant player's needs and quality standards. In Japan, this form of network is known as a *keiretsu*. It differs from the style of working in the Western car industry where dominant players tend to switch from supplier to supplier to drive down costs. However, although the dominated network is a model appropriate for a manufacturing business, it is not particularly relevant for a knowledge business.

The equal partner network

An equal partner network consists of several autonomous individuals or organisations, none of which is dominant, nor do they wish to cede much power to any organising force. Although individual members in this type of network can be strongly competitive, such networks exist primarily to encourage the exchange of ideas, and to share common services such as marketing or advertising. For instance, a group of craft workers in the Outer Hebrides making Harris Tweed, a product with a strong image and brand, might form an equal partner network.

In the health sector, public health professionals and organisations with values of independence and equality would be likely to find this type of network attractive because it has the advantage of a high degree of flexibility. However, an equal partner network lacks the leadership necessary to give it strategic direction, and does not provide the type of decision-making that may be necessary in difficult circumstances.

Community of practice

If a network consists of individuals, it can be referred to as a community of practice. A community of practice has been defined as:

people who share a concern, a set of problems, or a passion about a topic, and who deepen their knowledge and expertise in this area by interacting on an ongoing basis. (15)

A community of practice is similar to an equal partner network. They evolve spontaneously. One of the classic articles on organisational management featured photocopier repair operatives, who developed their own network and techniques of dealing with difficult repair problems and difficult customers. This community of practice existed in parallel to the official company repair manuals and protocols, but provided support to frontline workers that greatly increased their effectiveness.

People in a community of practice usually all belong to the same occupational group, but it is also possible for communities of practice to develop that cut across occupational groups or different functions within an organisation. The contribution that the coffee room or canteen plays in developing communities of practice should not be underestimated, emphasising the importance of informal face-to-face contact in the development of these communities. This effect needs to be replicated with virtual 'coffee rooms' on the World Wide Web.

The part that social media, notably facebook and twitter, can play is increasingly being recognised, although the fact that these media are being used by an age-group different to that managing the services within the system needs to be acknowledged and addressed. However, the use of tools such as Wikis to enable people to communicate, collaborate and create without having to meet in person is essential, and the older generation may have to be given the skills to use them. The use of such tools and the creation of a sense of purpose within the network allows it to become what has been called a community of influence, which is more than a community of practice:

> *Communities of Influence takes the communities of practice discussion in a new direction: what if you want to create a particular group (professional or lay) not just to share knowledge (as a community of practice does) but also to influence practice and policy? How are communities of influence best created and sustained? And is it possible to trace their influence over time?* (16)

The coordinated network

A coordinated network is one in which:

- there is no dominant member;
- there are clear strategies and directions;
- members have a degree of explicit contractual relationships, clear entry and exit criteria, and explicit rules, including rules for rule-making;
- there is acknowledged leadership.

Although some members of a coordinated network have more power than others, this power is ceded to them by all the network members. Members who have power, in the form of responsibility for one or more functions, are accountable to the membership as a whole. Although a coordinated network operates on explicit rules and contracts, it is equally dependent on trust. The trust a new member invests in the network can be strengthened by good experiences of networking, and by specific interventions designed to support the relationships among members. Trust can also be quickly lost.

Network management

In the systematic literature review of networks in the public and private sectors (14), ten 'key lessons' for network management were identified, and are summarised below.

1. The coordinator should aim to achieve a position of centrality within the network.
2. Have a clear mission statement and unambiguous rules of engagement.
3. Be inclusive – ensure all agencies and individuals gain ownership of the network.
4. Large networks should be avoided – they incur high administrative costs and lead to inertia.
5. Develop strategies for network cohesion.
6. Ownership may be facilitated by formalised contracts and agreements.
7. Actively engage respected professional leaders who will promote the network to peers.
8. Avoid network capture by, for example, a professional elite or a dominant organisational culture.
9. Respond to the needs of network members in such a way that the network remains relevant and worthwhile.
10. Professionals in networks must provide the mandate to allow managers to manage and govern their activities.

Good communication is the key to success

A system of care is delivered by a network of individuals and organisations. Systems and networks are based on and exist through relationships, relationships between separate services or individual professionals. Relationships depend on communication. In setting up systems and networks, therefore, it is necessary to focus on communication, because good communication is necessary to make a system work. Without good communication, the system and the network do not exist.

In teams, the main mode of communication is face to face. However, problems in face-to-face communication are common, and poor communication is one of the main reasons for patients' complaints and management problems. In networks, not only is communication different, the whole process of joint working is different. A distinction can be made between two types of group-working: traditional and virtual. It should be noted that virtual is not the opposite of traditional; 'virtual' can be considered as the opposite of 'real'.

In a table from the book called *The Virtual Edge* (17), the characteristics of 'traditional' and 'virtual' processes are contrasted and compared. Virtual teams need to adopt different ways of working that rely much less on face-to-face interaction when compared with traditional teams (Table 6.1).

Using information technology to manage systems

The role of information technology in systems development

It is possible to develop systems in the absence of information technology. Smallpox was eradicated before computers played an important part in healthcare management or the delivery of public health services. However, information technology plays a very important part in enabling systems to be developed and sustained, and the impact of information technology is increasing as the Internet becomes ubiquitous.

Manuel Castells has argued that society is in its Third Industrial Revolution (18). Although Castells does not focus on healthcare, his analysis is relevant and can be adapted to describe the revolutions in healthcare.

- The First Healthcare Revolution, from 1850 to 1950, was based largely on empirical analysis and common-sense. The most obvious example is the map of cholera cases around the Broad Street pump that led John Snow to conclude that cholera was a waterborne disease, and to take the necessary action, long before the bacterium that causes cholera had been identified.

- The Second Healthcare Revolution, from 1950 onwards, was based on science – physics, chemistry and high-quality engineering. It gave us some of the marvels of the second half of the 20th century:

Table 6.1: Comparing traditional and virtual processes (17)

Traditional	Virtual
Co-located resources	Distributed, technically connected resources
Serial, sequential work	Parallel, simultaneous at times
Ad hoc communications	Continuous, anytime communications
Face-to-face discussions	Non-real time chat sessions
Paper exchange	Electronic document exchange
Distribution processes	Global access of information
Individual task work	Continuous sharing of tasks and dependencies
Local information storage	Global information repository
Questionable, unworkable processes	Processes that support virtual work
Working solo	Collaboration
Competition and distrust	Teamwork and trust
Decision-making from the top	Team decision-making

magnetic resonance imaging (MRI), anti-psychotics, antibiotics, hip replacement, chemotherapy, antidepressants, randomised controlled trials, and systematic reviews.

- The Third Healthcare Revolution has already started, driven not by scientists and clinicians, but by three other forces – citizens, knowledge, and information technology (IT) (Figure 6.5). (18)

Information technology is evolving at speed, and becoming both ubiquitous and invisible. When Tim Berners Lee was asked in the Millennium issue of *Wired* what he hoped for by 2010, he said he hoped that no-one would be using the term 'the Internet' by 2010 because, like electricity, it would be universally available. This is almost what has happened, although people still do refer to the

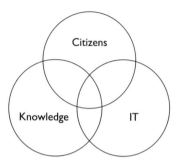

Figure 6.5 Drivers of the Third Healthcare Revolution

Internet. The Internet led to the development of the World Wide Web, which in turn led to the development of smart 'phones that are easier to use. In fact, it is the mobile 'phone that is the radical, revolutionary development, what Clayton Christensen calls a 'disruptive' innovation (19), because it has made knowledge, both good and bad, universally available.

'Disruptive' innovations, such as the mobile 'phone, change the paradigm of a business. There are two types of change:

1. change within the existing paradigm – a first-order change;
2. systemic change, that is, the creation of a new paradigm – a second-order or radical change.

The development of systems offers the opportunity for both first- and second-order change. To undertake a radical or second-order change, it is necessary to create what Clayton Christensen calls the 'third enabler of disruption', that is:

> ... the coalescence of an independent value network around the new disruptive business models through which care is delivered. Disruptions are rarely plug-compatible with the prior value network, or commercial ecosystem. When disruptive innovators assume that relying on the existing value network is a cheaper, faster way to succeed, they invariably find that ensconcing their 'piece' of the system into the old value network kills their innovation – or it co-opts and reshapes their disruptive business model so that it conforms to that system. Vice versa never happens. (19)

Disruptiveness is a cultural feature of a network, and can be found irrespective of the style of management of the network. In *The Innovator's Dilemma*, Christensen (20) describes how 'disruptive' innovations create dilemmas for those who run successful companies. The book is subtitled *When New Technologies Cause Great Companies to Fail*, and demonstrates how the innate caution of some senior executives faced with a disruptive technology they did not wish to recognise contributed to their failure. Christensen's book has been influential, and the concept of disruptive innovations or technology has entered the language of those responsible for managing organisations.

Although technology facilitates the development of systems and networks, it also creates social change. First published in 1982, one of the classics of the management literature, *Corporate Cultures: The rites and rituals of a corporate life* by Terrence Deal and Allan Kennedy, describes how the work of big organisations will be done in small, autonomous units linked to the mega-corporation by new telecommunications and computer technologies (21). Deal and Kennedy emphasise that '*the business of change is cultural transformation*', and the Internet has changed culture by its very existence.

In their book, *The Knowledge Creating Company*, Ikujiro Nonaka and Hirotaka Takeuchi made detailed studies of companies, such as Honda, Sharp and Matsushita, and concluded that the most appropriate name for this type of organisation is a 'hypertext' organisation (see Figure 4.2). (5) In this context, the term 'hypertext' used by Nonaka and Takeuchi describes a knowledge-based system. In knowledge-based systems, it is knowledge that binds people, not bureaucratic power.

'Hypertext' is one of the plethora of new terms to describe features of the Internet. Many of the terms are metaphors, such as platform, menu and window. Hypertext is non-linear, and information is accessed through nodes that the user can navigate in any order. In contrast, linear text such as this book is sequential, presented in an order defined by the creator of the material. Hierarchies use linear text to communicate from top to bottom and, less commonly, from bottom to top. Networks are strengthened, and indeed created, by hypertext. Other terms that have been use to describe 'hypertext' or knowledge-based organisations are shown in Box 6.1. (17)

Box 6.1 Names for the new type of organisation in the knowledge era (17)

- Fishnet
- Network
- Virtual
- Irrational
- Three-dimensional
- Hypertextual
- Adhocratic
- Intelligent
- Transcendent
- Learning
- Imaginary
- Knowledge-rich

Knowledge-based organisations have also been called 'networked information economies' – an economy is a network of organisations, teams, and individuals. In *The Wealth of Networks,* Benkler describes the distinguishing characteristics of a networked information economy:

> *The fundamental elements of the difference between the networked information economy and the mass media are network architecture and the cost of becoming a speaker. The first element is the shift from a hub-and-spoke architecture with unidirectional links to the end points in the mass media, to distributed architecture with multidirectional connections among all nodes in the networked information environment.* (22)

The impact of technology on organisations is the subject of continuing debate among historians. At one end of the spectrum are the determinists, those who argue that technology is the principal driver of social change. One of the most famous books in this field, *Medieval Technology and Social Change* (23), describes the position clearly. White argued that the manorial system of land-holding arose because the invention of the heavy plough forced villages to work their oxen in teams to draw the plough through the thick clay of northern Europe. The principles behind White's argument hold true for the 20th century. Analogous developments in healthcare would be the introduction of linear accelerators in cancer care, and dialysis machines in kidney care, which created networks of professionals. Such networks did not evolve in specialties where there was no technology requiring the investment of large amounts of capital.

At the other end of the spectrum are those who accept that technology initiates change, but believe that human beings also shape the use of the technology. Some of the classic research on this topic – the study of Durham miners – was conducted by Trist et al. at the Tavistock Institute (a partner institute of the famous Tavistock Clinic, which promoted the use of psychotherapy in the NHS). This study led to the description of a socio-technical system.

The concept of a production system as a socio-technical system designates a general field of study concerned with the interrelations of the technical and socio-psychological organization of industrial production systems. . . . The concept of a socio-technical system arose from the consideration that any production system requires both a technological organization – equipment and process layout – and a work organization relating to each other those who carry out the necessary tasks. The technological demands place limits on the type of work organization possible, but a work organization has social and psychological properties of its own that are independent of technology. . . . A socio-technical system must also satisfy the financial conditions of the industry of which it is a part. It must have economic validity. It has in fact social, technological and economic dimensions, all of which are interdependent but all of which have independent values of their own. (24)

The clinical network in the age of the Internet is an excellent example of a socio-technical system.

Developing information subsystems for systems management

What part do 'information systems' play?

Although the term 'information system' is widely used in healthcare, any information system is really a *sub*system of a greater clinical system. Although an information system can be said to have a life of its own, as may a laboratory or an imaging service, these are examples of cross-cutting services in a matrix of care. It is very important for laboratory, imaging, pharmacy, and information services, as well as other functional services, to work using systems methods. When we use the term 'system' in healthcare, we should give priority to the core business of healthcare, to bipolar depression, Parkinson's disease or rheumatoid arthritis, for example.

The relationship between these two types of organisations needs to be managed as a matrix, as shown in Figure 6.6. Matrix management is fundamental to all complex businesses (25).

Functional Services \ Core Businesses	Stroke	Breast Cancer	Bipolar Depression	Epilepsy
Laboratory				
Imaging				
Finance				
IT				
Personnel				

Figure 6.6 Matrix showing functional services in relation to systems of care – healthcare's 'core' businesses

One of the problems faced by people delivering information systems and information technology to healthcare is the fact that they are often asked to put a healthcare information technology solution into chaos. On occasion, the introduction of a computer can bring everyone to their senses and lead to the development of a clinical system, but that is rare. In a project designed to evaluate the prescribing and dispensing of medicines, it was found that widely differing methods were used in adjacent hospital wards. In one ward, a book was used; in another, the ward sister had a 'system' of Post-it® notes and reminders attached to the drugs trolley. The introduction of information technology to such chaos can make things worse, and the information technology supplier can receive the blame unfairly (26).

It is impossible to install information technology unless clinical systems have been designed and built, but it is also impossible to manage systems without information technology.

How the Map of Medicine facilitates systems building

One tool that has been used to accelerate the development of healthcare systems and to sustain the systems that have been developed is the Map of Medicine. The Map presents knowledge in the form of care pathways, which can be viewed by both primary and secondary care clinicians on the World Wide Web.

The Map of Medicine originated from a sense of frustration experienced by Owen Epstein, a consultant physician at the Royal Free Hospital in Hampstead, north London. Epstein had noticed a significant increase in referrals for abdominal pain to his Gastro-enterology Service. The usual response of clinicians to an increase in demand is to increase supply, but he came to the conclusion that more of the same was not the appropriate response. He surmised that, if the general practitioners referring these additional cases knew what he knew, they would not need to refer all of those patients to him. His response was to develop the idea of a digital care pathway, which included clear indications for referral.

The Royal Free Hospital is part of University College London (UCL), which has a service to help UCL Faculty staff and NHS consultants with academic links to UCL to develop their ideas, and 'bring them to market'. The finance necessary to build the software for constructing digital care pathways was from two sources: the UCL Development Fund, and the foundation set up with the profits from Factor VIII (the anti-clotting factor for treating haemophilia discovered at the Royal Free Hospital many years ago). Using these resources, the software system known as the Map of Medicine was created.

The advantages of the Map of Medicine hosted on the World Wide Web are numerous:

- a long document (100–200 pages) can be distilled into a small number of pathways;
- it can cut across the considerable barrier that all too often exists between primary and secondary care;
- any 'national' pathway can be 'localised' or adapted to practice in a particular geographical area or for a particular population; thus, people who want to use the Map in Northumberland, Cornwall or Manchester, or New Zealand or Italy, can add their own variations to the pathway:
  - if a particular resource is available locally, such as a randomised controlled trial currently recruiting patients, a node can easily be inserted by a clinician, with librarian support;
  - if there is a resource over which patients can exercise choice, such as joining a patient support group, this can be added into a pathway;
  - if a particular resource is not available locally, such as a PET scan, this can be removed.

'The Map is wrong'

It is not uncommon, when presenting a version of the Map that has been developed nationally or in another healthcare system, for at least one clinician to say 'The Map is wrong'. What the clinician usually means is 'The Map expresses something different from my way of doing things'. When it is pointed out that this version of the Map has been prepared by other clinicians, food for thought is generated. Many clinicians are not aware of precisely how other clinicians manage a problem; even clinicians at the same hospital or in the same clinical team may manage the same problem in different ways. There are several reasons for this:

- one team may base its practice on a different evidence base from others;
- owing to the tedium and inexactitude of having to describe one's clinical practice in words, it is difficult to identify variations in

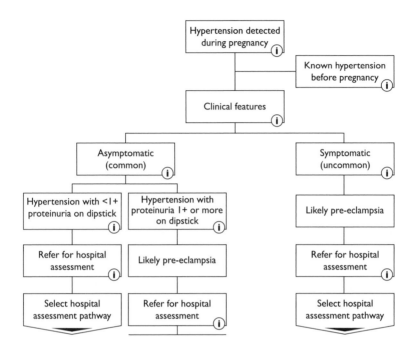

Figure 6.7 Part of The Map of Medicine® for hypertension detected during pregnancy

practice that may have evolved as a result of chance or been indoctrinated through different training programmes.

When clinical practice is presented in a diagrammatic form like the Map (Figure 6.7), it is immediately obvious to any clinician how the Map differs from their own practice. It is also immediately obvious to every patient what route they should follow along the pathway. By giving the Map to patients, they can become more responsible for their journey through the network.

No clinician is an island entire of itself.

Questions for reflection when teaching or developing networks

If using these questions during network building or teaching, give one of the questions to the group and ask them to work in pairs to reflect on the question for three minutes; try to get people who do not know one another to work together. When taking feedback, let each pair make only one point. In the interests of equity, if you start with the pair on the left-hand side of the room for the first question, start with the pair on the right-hand side of the room for the second question.

- If you were looking at the annual reports of two services for asthma in competition for your personal care, what would be the most important criteria that would influence your decision?
- What characteristics are needed to be a good leader of a clinical network?
- How would you use the Internet to make your clinical network more effective?

References

(1) Williamson, O. E. and Masten, S. E. (editors) (1999) *The Economics of Transaction Costs.* Edward Elgar Publishing Ltd.
(2) Ostrom, E. (1990) *Governing the Commons: The Evolution of Institutions for Collective Action.* Cambridge University Press.
(3) Hölldobler, B. and Wilson, E. O. (1990) *The Ants.* Springer-Verlag.
(4) Dick, M. for the UK Forum on Haemoglobin Disorders (2010) *Sickle Cell Disease in Childhood. Standards and Guidelines of Care.* Second edition. NHS Sickle Cell and Thalassaemia Screening Programme in partnership with the Sickle Cell Society. Available at: http://sct.screening.nhs.uk/cms.php?folder=2493
(5) Nonaka, I. and Takeuchi, H. (1995) *The Knowledge-Creating Company: How Japanese Companies Create the Dynamics of Innovation.* Seventh edition. Oxford University Press, USA.
(6) Morgan, J. M. and Liker, J. K. (2006) *The Toyota Product Development System. Integrating People, Process, and Technology.* Productivity Press, New York.

(7) Nelson, E. C., Batalden, P. B. and Godfrey, M. M. (2007) *Quality by Design. A Clinical Microsystems Approach.* Jossey-Bass.

(8) Simon, H. A. (1997) *Administrative Behavior. A Study of Decision-Making Processes In Administrative Organizations.* Fourth edition. The Free Press.

(9) Etzioni, A. (1975) *A comparative analysis of complex organizations.* The Free Press.

(10) Porter, M. E. and Teisberg, E. O. (2006) *Redefining Health Care: Creating Value-Based Competition on Results.* Harvard Business School Press.

(11) Berwick, D. M. (2008) The science of improvement. *JAMA* 299: 1182–1184. doi: 10.1001/jama.299.10.1182

(12) Pawson, R. and Tilley, N. (1997) *Realistic Evaluation.* Sage Publications Ltd.

(13) Gray, J. A. M., Patnick, J. and Blanks, R. G. (2007) Maximising benefit and minimising harm of screening. *Br. Med. J.* 336: 480–483. doi: 10.1136/bmj.39470.643218.94 (Published 28 February 2008)

(14) Howarth, A. (2004) *Key lessons for network management in health care.* Networks Briefing. NHS Service Delivery and Organisation R&D Programme. Available at: http://www.sdo.nihr.ac.uk/files/project/ SDO_BP_08-1218-039_V01.pdf

(15) Wenger, E., McDermott, R. and Snyder, W. M. (2002) *Cultivating Communities of Practice. A Guide to Managing Knowledge.* Harvard Business School Press.

(16) Donaldson, A., Lank, E. and Maher, J. (2011) *Communities of Influence. Improving healthcare through conversations and connections.* Radcliffe Publishing Ltd.

(17) Mayer, M. (1998) *The Virtual Edge. Embracing Technology for Distributed Project Team Success.* Project Management Institute Communications Office, US.

(18) Stalder, F. (2006) *Manual Castells. The Theory of the Network Society.* Polity Press.

(19) Christensen, C. M. (2009) *The Innovator's Prescription. A Disruptive Solution for Health Care.* Harper Business Essentials.

(20) Christensen, C. M. (1997) *The Innovator's Dilemma. When New Technologies Cause Great Firms to Fail.* Harper Business School Press.

(21) Deal, T. E. and Kennedy, A. A. (1982) *Corporate Cultures. The Rites and Rituals of Corporate Life.* Basic Books

(22) Benkler, Y. (2006) *The Wealth of Networks. How Social Production Transforms Markets and Freedom.* Yale University Press.

(23) White, L. Jr (1964) *Medieval Technology and Social Change.* Oxford University Press.

(24) Trist, E. L., Higgin, G. W., Murray, H. and Pollock, A. B. (1963) *Organizational Choice. Capabilities of groups at the coal face under changing technologies. The loss, re-discovery and transformation of a work tradition.* Tavistock Publications.

(25) Grove, A. S. (1995) *High Output Management.* Vintage Books.
(26) Bates, D. W., Teich, J. M., Lee, J., Serger, D., Kuperman, G. J., Ma'Luf, N., Boyle, D. and Leape, L. (1999) The impact of computerized physician order entry on medication error prevention. *J. Am. Med. Inform. Assoc.* 6: 313–321.

7

HOW TO DEVELOP A SYSTEMS CULTURE

This chapter will:

- define culture;
- emphasise the importance of culture change;
- describe how leaders can influence culture.

By the end of the chapter you will have developed an understanding of:

- the relationship between systems and culture;
- how to explain the need to develop a new culture to colleagues;
- the importance of language in creating or changing culture.

Touchstone: Reversing healthcare's inverse laws

The Inverse Care Law, first enunciated by Julian Tudor Hart (1), states that the amount of care provided is inversely related to the need for care.

Taking this as a blueprint, it is possible to propose an Inverse Attention Law, in which the amount of attention devoted to structure, systems and culture is inversely related to their importance. Structure is the least important aspect of an organisation, but it receives the most attention from everyone.

What about systems and culture? Until recently, systems probably received more attention than culture, but culture is moving up the agenda rapidly, and rightly so. Although this is a book about systems, culture is the most important aspect of an organisation, and should receive more attention than systems.

However, systems and culture are interwoven like warp and weft: a change in one affects the other, and the leaders of 21st century healthcare need to manage both.
Over the next decade, we must work to make the Inverse Attention Law redundant.

The culture of an organisation has been defined by Edgar Schein, as:

> *a pattern of shared basic assumptions that was learned by a group as it solved its problems of external adaptation and internal integration, that has worked well enough to be considered valid and, therefore, to be taught to new members as the correct way to perceive, think, and feel in relation to those problems.* (2)

In colloquial terms, it can be encapsulated as 'The way we do things around here'.

The culture necessary for an effective system is one in which:

- everyone is respected and of equal importance, including patients;
- feedback is welcomed as a source of learning;
- the focus is on value, with a hatred of waste;
- innovation is sought, and technology is used appropriately;
- knowledge is managed at least as carefully as money.

It is the responsibility of the leaders in the network of organisations involved in a system to create this culture through:

- what they know;
- what they believe to be important;
- what they say;
- how they behave.

There are practical steps that can be taken to facilitate the development of a culture:

- using a new language, such as 'system', 'network' and 'node';
- stopping the use of unhelpful terms such as 'hub and spoke' or 'academic medical centre';

- creating a common conceptual base, for instance, that all the people who manage resources in the network are familiar with Donabedian's concept of optimality (3), even if they have not read his books;
- ensuring that the terms in common use, such as 'efficiency' or 'quality', are invested with the same meaning by all who use them.

The creation of a healthcare system is as much about the socialisation of all the people involved, including patients, through a common culture as it is about the management of services.

Developing systems requires a change of heart as well as a change of mind. It is to do with feeling as well as thinking, and some people will not be able to make the transition from hierarchy to system. Hence, the old management adage:

For some people, one has to accept that while there is retirement there is hope.

Management and policy-making as activities are driven by words and, sometimes, numbers. The belief in the power of words to effect change is reinforced by a professional's education, which is usually mainly verbal. Education and training is designed to give people knowledge and to develop their skills, based on the theory that given these intellectual stimuli change will be brought about.

However, another powerful force for change is technology. In *Medieval Technology and Social Change* (4), Lynn White Jr argues that most of history has been recorded by 'scribblers', people who can read and write. In the past these scribblers, priests and politicians emphasised the importance of words in changing society. Although White highlights the other powerful forces that have shaped society, including technology, he also outlines the problem in determining the contribution technology has made to changing society. The people who developed early technologies, such as the stirrup or the heavy plough, could not write. Therefore, they left no record of their plans, and no description of the state of society before the technology was introduced, or the impact on society afterwards. Even in the 20th century, people responsible for developing technologies, such as hip replacement or statins, were too busy to write about it. By comparison, the people developing intellectual values for healthcare, such as 'equality' or 'quality', existed in a world of words and ideas, and wrote about these concepts and the influence they had on shaping healthcare.

> Culture eats strategy for breakfast, but it eats structure for breakfast, lunch, and dinner.

Questions for reflection when teaching or developing networks

If using these questions during network building or teaching, give one of the questions to the group and ask them to work in pairs to reflect on the question for three minutes; try to get people who do not know one another to work together.

When taking feedback, let each pair make only one point. In the interests of equity, if you start with the pair on the left-hand side of the room for the first question, start with the pair on the right-hand side of the room for the second question.

- What would you ask clinicians to help you ascertain whether an organisation had a collaborative systems culture?
- What words would you choose to describe the culture of a system that is working well?
- How would you get a group of busy clinicians to define what is meant by the culture of a service?

References

(1) Tudor Hart, J. (1971) Inverse Care Law. *Lancet* i; 405–412.
(2) Schein, E. H. (2004) *Organizational Culture and Leadership*. Third edition. Jossey-Bass.
(3) Donabedian, A. (1966) Evaluating the Quality of Medical Care. *The Milbank Memorial Fund Quarterly* 44; 166–203.
(4) White, L. Jr (1964) *Medieval Technology and Social Change*. Oxford University Press.

CODA

WHAT IS THE BEST METAPHOR FOR A SYSTEM?

Metaphor: the figure of speech in which a name or descriptive term is transferred to some object to which it is not properly applicable; the example given is '*Life is a Pilgrimage*'.

Shorter Oxford English Dictionary

High on the 'favourites' lists of management books is *Images of Organization* by Gareth Morgan (1). In this work, Morgan summarises and analyses the metaphors that have been used in the last century to describe organisations. He demonstrates how the metaphors in common use have changed as the prevailing theory about how organisations work has changed, with theory replacing theory in an intellectual analogue of biological evolution, most famously described by Thomas Kuhn in his classic *The Structure of Scientific Revolutions* (2).

In the early days of the car industry production line, Frederick Winslow Taylor, who published *The Principles of Scientific Management* in 1911, described the factory as a giant machine (3). As a result, the prevailing metaphor became the machine – organisations were machines and human beings but cogs within them, exemplified by Adam Smith's analysis of the manufacture of pins, and captured on the back of the £20 note. Other metaphors followed: the organisation as a family, and the organisation as a brain, to give but two examples.

So, which metaphor is most appropriate for the system? Perhaps it is 'network'.

In this book, we have had to distinguish between a system and a network as if they are different entities, but without a network there is no system. The meanings of the word 'network' in the *Shorter Oxford English Dictionary* are:

work in which thread, wires or the like are arranged in the form of a net, or a complex system of rivers, canals, railways, wireless transmitting stations, etc.

However, there is a third meaning offered: it is '*a piece of work having this form*', first used in 1590.

So, it would seem that the word was already being used as a metaphor in the 16th century: the system is a network.

References

(1) Morgan, G. (2006) *Images of Organization.* Sage Publications.
(2) Kuhn, T. S. (1996) *The Structure of Scientific Revolutions.* Third edition. University of Chicago Press.
(3) Taylor, F. W. (original date of publication 1911; reprinted 2007) *The Principles of Scientific Management.* BiblioBazaar.

Index

Page numbers in **bold** type refer to figures, those in **_bold italic_** refer to tables, and those in _italics_ refer to quotations.